STANLEY GIBBONS

Coll
British a
Telephone Cards

CW00920295

S.E.R. HISCOCKS

Stanley Gibbons Publications Limited · Ringwood & London

Published by

Stanley Gibbons Publications Limited
Parkside
Christchurch Road
Ringwood
Hants. BH24 3SH
England

in association with

Dr S.E.R.Hiscocks
P.O.Box 77
Woking
Surrey, GU22 0HB
England

Printed by

Acorn Litho Colour Printers Ltd
The Foxwood Press,
Old Woking,
Surrey,
GU22 9LH
England.

CONTENTS

ACKNOWLEDGEMENTS

In compiling this book I have received generous help from many friends in
the telephone companies, the manufacturing companies and the hobby
including:

Jo Anderson and Richard Kew of British Telecom,

Valerie O'Leary, Jennifer Freeman, Daniel Reed, Sarah Taylor, Ian MacIsaac
and others of Mercury,

Barry Laine and Ann Warren of IPL and Alan Weldon of IPL (Scotland),

Frank Lynch and Peter Richardson of Telecom Eireann,

Jim Hoskinson and Chris Carter of Manx Telecom,

Guy Pipon and his colleagues of Jersey Telecom,

Mary Radcliffe, Douglas Genders, Dave Price and Jane Windsor
of Landis and Gyr (UK),

Carol Sweeney, Caroline Hepburn, Jerry Macusker and others of GPT,

Alex Henneberg and Alex Findlay of Paytelco,

Dev Sooranna, Peter Harradine, Andrew Goodall, Peter Snow, Eric Elias and
Peter Sharman, all of the Telephone Card Club, who helped me to set the
prices and provided much information on control number and other varieties,

and many other friends who generously provided information, lent me cards
to illustrate and generally made my task possible. I am most grateful to
all of them.

INTRODUCTION

This book aims to provide a fairly specialised listing of all telephone cards which have been issued in Great Britain and Ireland and which have been available to the public.

As the collecting of telephone cards becomes ever more popular, so the ways in which people like to collect become more varied. Many are happy to have one of each basic type and do not bother with variations of shade, control numbers or notch. Others like to take all major and minor variations into account in building a highly specialised collection. There is, of course, no 'right' way to collect collecting is a hobby which you pursue for enjoyment and whatever degree of specialisation you choose is right for you.

I have said above that one collects telephone cards for enjoyment and that is true but one should not forget the investment potential. If the prices in this book are compared with those quoted in the world catalogue published less than a year ago as The Stanley Gibbons Catalogue of Telephone Cards it will be seen that many have risen considerably. This is inevitable when the numbers of collectors is rising and the numbers of discontinued cards is static. One should not despair however. The cards which you buy, find or obtain by exchange today may in a couple of years' time be approaching the values of those that today seem to be out of reach.

Collecting does not have to be expensive. Some collectors like to have one of each batch of 100,000 British Telecom cards as shown by the first four characters in the control number on the reverse of each card and these can be obtained very cheaply if not all that easily. For this reason we have devoted a couple of pages to as complete a listing of known control prefixes as I and more knowledgeable colleagues in the (UK) Telephone Card Collectors' Club can make it. Similarly all known control types on Mercury cards are listed in the text.

ABOUT THIS BOOK

All cards issued to the public and to closed user groups are listed. The only cards not listed are those bearing the names of individuals which are used as visiting cards, mostly by senior staff in the telephone companies.

TYPES OF CARDS

Cards are listed under several categories. The ordinary everyday cards which continue in use for considerable periods of time and are reprinted as required are known as 'Definitive' cards and are normally given D numbers. 'Special' cards (S prefixes) are generally commemorative, decorative or thematic and form a specific issue which are available through normal channels along with the Definitives and which will not be reprinted when used up. 'Advertising' cards (prefixed A) normally advertise a commercial product, service or event and are generally not available through normal channels one usually has to buy the product concerned to obtain them. 'Private' cards (prefixed P) are sponsored by some individual or organisation, generally in small quantities such as 1000. Fortunately Mercury has adopted a policy of printing a further 4000 or so of such cards so that collectors can always obtain them at face value at the time of issue. 'Promotional' cards are produced by the card or telephone manufacturers to demonstrate their systems at exhibitions and other points of sale and are generally available only to people attending the exhibitions. 'Closed User Group' cards are available only to those at a specific location such as a prison, military base or oil platform. Finally a new category has been introduced for cards which are not personal but which were never issued to the public. These are called 'Internal' cards and include the special set given by Manx Telecom to all its staff to commemorate completion of the modernisation of their system and the so-called 'party card' which Mercury gave to those invited to a Christmas party in 1989.

USING THIS BOOK

Each card is given a catalogue number and this is the letter and number at the extreme left of each listing. You will find the cards listed in advertisements and auction catalogues by this number. The next number, which is in **bold italics**, is that of the illustration of the card. The procedure has been changed from that used in my earlier catalogues in that, to avoid confusion, **the illustration number is now always the same as that of the card illustrated.** If the illustration number is in brackets, e.g. *(S57)*, it means that the card looks like that illustration but differs in some respect – usually in the value printed on it or in something printed on the reverse which cannot be seen in the illustration. The next number across the page is the face value of the card. If no currency symbol is given it is in telephone time units as in British Telecom cards. Next comes the date of issue and then the name of the card if it has one and its colours. This is followed by a figure in brackets which is the number of that card issued or printed an important figure because it shows how rare the card is or will be. The control number type or prefix may then be given.

PRICES

Finally, at the extreme right, we have the collectors' value of the card or the price you might hope to see paid for the card in an auction or to pay for it from a dealer. It is not, of course, the price that a dealer will offer you for it. The price for common cards is normally given at 50 pence but this incorporates an element of 'handling charge' real values are smaller but indeterminate. If one can tell by looking at the card (that is without access to a telephone which accepts the card) whether the card has been used or not then two separate values are given for mint (unused) and used cards. British Telecom, Jersey and some Irish cards therefore have two values given. If it is not possible to tell by eye whether they have been used or not they are given a single value which is, in effect, the value of an unused card or of a used card in perfect condition. If it can be seen that such a card has not been used, for example because it is still sealed in a special packet, a premium might be expected but few cards are available in this condition so prices are not specifically listed for sealed cards. The prices quoted represent the market values so far as these can be judged at the time of going to press but prices are moving all the time and these prices could be out of date soon. If no price is given it is because cards are not normally available in that condition or because the card is so rare that no market price has yet been established.

HOW TO OBTAIN CARDS

Basically one can find them near payphones, one can buy them or one can obtain them by exchange with other collectors. Most of us do all three. There is an active Telephone Card Club of (at the time of writing) some 175 members in the UK which issues very helpful newsletters and makes it easy to locate fellow collectors to exchange cards. There are also periodic bourses at which many dealers and collectors buy, sell and exchange cards.

MINT OR USED CARDS

It is for the collector to decide whether to collect cards in unused or used condition or in both. Generally the difference in value between used and unused is more marked in cards where it can easily be seen which is which - the optical cards and the Jersey GPT cards which have a use-indication system which makes a small dent in the card against a scale on the reverse at the end of each call. Other GPT cards are now becoming available in sealed collectors' packets at a premium and it remains to be seen whether these will be greatly sought after in this condition. British Telecom cards are often collected as supplied in sealed sachets.

HOW TO STORE YOUR CARDS

Most collectors now use albums containing special leaves designed to take telephone cards. These can be bought from Stanley Gibbons or from other dealers around the world. There is some concern over whether the plasticisers in PVC plastics can damage cards or alter their colours but there has so far been no firm evidence of this ever having occurred. Polypropylene leaves may be safer in this respect but they do tend to be a little less transparent. GPT cards are laminated and it is most unlikely that they would be affected by PVC. The control numbers on Autelca and some earlier Plessey (now GPT) cards may however be vulnerable.

PERIPHERALS

Some collectors also collect special envelopes in which cards are obtained such as on railways, at sporting events and bearing advertisements. These are not listed in this book but they can be quite expensive. Point-of-sale advertising material, leaflets and similar card-related items are also collected.

SOME TELEPHONE CARD TERMS EXPLAINED

This book is intended both for the experienced collector and the beginner. For the latter it might be useful if a few of the terms used in the book are explained.

Telephone Card. In this book the term means a prepayment card. It will have a set number of units or cash value programmed into a memory of some sort and these will be progressively deleted in use such that the card is finally exhausted and of no further use in a telephone. Telephone credit and charge transfer cards are not included in this book.

Optical Cards. These are the cards as used by British Telecom and by most of the oil companies on their offshore platforms. They are manufactured by Landis and Gyr in London or Switzerland. In use, a laser beam shines through the black plastic (which is transparent in the infra-red) onto a pattern embossed in a strip of metal. If the pattern is right (i.e. the card is indeed intended for that telephone), the light is reflected to a detector for a period of time after which a hot point touches the pattern from above and destroys it. The laser then moves on to the next bit of pattern until all are used up and the card is fully used. Whether a card has been used or not can be seen by holding the card at the correct angle to the light when the little marks made by the hot probe in cancelling the units can usually be seen. The large number of unused units found on cards by collectors suggests that many people are not aware of this.

Optical Track. This is the strip of metallic foil on which the pattern on an optical card is embossed. It runs across the card about 15mm from the top edge. It is covered by paint and cannot normally be seen on early cards which had a "short track" ending inside the margins of the design. Later cards have a "long track" and the ends of the track can be seen projecting into the margins beyond the colour.

Band or Optical Band. This is the strip of colour which covers the optical track and should not be confused with the track itself. It is a green silk-screened band on BT cards although most other countries have a special white band of 'thermographic' paint which goes black when the hot probe touches it to show more clearly how much of the card has been used. Only the earlier Shell Expro and the Irish Galway cards in this book have such white bands. The optical bands can vary in width and people collect cards with different band widths.

Control Numbers. These are the numbers placed on the cards by the manufacturers to identify each individual card. On Landis and Gyr (optical) cards they are impressed on the back in, usually, the bottom right corner. Some collectors identify up to five different fonts (sizes and shapes of digits) in these controls and they may also be upright (called 'normal') or upside down ('inverted'). On GPT cards (Mercury, Isle of Man, Jersey and some Irish) they are printed on the backs, usually at the top although earlier ones were often at the bottom. The earlier GPT controls were in purple on black and need to be held at the right angle to the light to be read. The Autelca cards used by IPL in the UK and in the Irish field trials have numbers printed on the front or back in various positions and in various fonts care should be taken with these since they can be wiped off. The French-made 'smart' cards now used in Ireland do not have controls so far although those used in France do have batch numbers.

Smart Cards. These are the electronic cards now used in Ireland. They have a silicon chip embedded in the card in which the units are stored. The actual chip can be seen through the resin on the reverse of a Schlumberger card but cannot be seen on a Gemplus card. The chip is connected to a gold (or sometimes, in the case of Schlumberger cards, silver) contact above the chip which can be of various shapes according to the manufacturer of the card. So far Ireland has not issued the same cards by different manufacturers but this often happens in France and the cards are then seen as quite different from a collecting point of view.

Notches. These are the small indentations usually on the right-hand edge of the card to allow blind users or anyone in the dark to know which way to insert the card into the telephone. Earlier BT cards did not have them and otherwise identical cards with and without notches are regarded as quite different. Occasionally Landis and Gyr cards are printed on inverted or upside-down blanks so that the notch appears in one of the three possible "wrong" positions – usually bottom left – and these are very rare. Watch out for forgeries! GPT cards (Mercury, I.O.M., Jersey and some Ireland) started out with large or deep notches and then changed to small or shallow notches. Some cards from the change-over period are found with either small or large notch and one type may be much more valuable than the other. Again, watch out for forgeries although the large and small notches occur at slightly different positions so a small notch cannot be changed into a convincing large notch. Always compare with a genuine large notch card. On the small notch cards there can be considerable variation in size (but not shape or position) due to variations in where the blank was trimmed and the notch may appear to be missing altogether although one can usually see a slight depression of the surface at the position at the edge of the card where the notch was before the edge was trimmed.

Steve Hiscocks

April, 1991

Following the privatisation of British Telecom and the ending of their monopoly, three telephone companies now operate payphone systems in the UK. Optical cards are manufactured by Landis and Gyr for British Telecom. Mercury Communications, a Cable and Wireless company, introduced payphones using GPT magnetic cards in London in 1988 and has since expanded to other UK cities and towns. A further company, International Payphones Ltd, introduced a second magnetic system for off-street applications (hospitals, shopping precincts, oil platforms, etc.) using Autelca telephones and cards in January, 1990. IPL has recently withdrawn from cardphones but IPL (Scotland) remains in offshore and special event cardphones.

BRITISH TELECOM

Earlier types (control numbers on reverse begin with letter G) were manufactured in Switzerland. Since March, 1983, many cards have been made in the UK and control numbers on the reverse have begun with three numerals followed by a letter and serial number. The first of the three numerals before the letter in the control number is the last digit of the year and the second two the month of manufacture. Thus '05' is May and '12' is December. The '0' may be substituted by any even number and the '1' by any odd number so '25' or '45' would also be May and '32' or '52' would also be December. 999 controls are arbitrarily used for very short runs – for some special cards like the 50,000,000th and also for ordinary cards made to replace defective cards to complete a batch. The latter are rare. UK-made cards can generally be distinguished from Swiss-made cards in that the former have the optical strip set into a shallow trough, often with ridges on either side, while the latter do not and the surface is thus flat and smooth. Cards are found with long or short optical tracks. The long tracks extend into the margins. There was a gradual change from short to long track but no particular pattern to their occurrence. The unit was originally £0.05 but it was increased after a short period to £0.10. The complimentary cards, of initially 10, later 5 and now 3 and 10 units, are given out by British Telecom to introduce new customers to the system and are also extensively used by British Telecom staff to replace faulty cards and for official purposes. The issue of advertising cards began at the end of 1986 and special or commemorative cards appeared in 1987.

C – COMPLIMENTARY CARDS

No.	Ill.	Units	Date	Description	Value	
C1	*C1*	5	11/85	Green / silver (1,600,000)	15.00 ☐	2.00 ☐
C2	*C2*	5	1/86	Green / silver (3,100,000)	1.00 ☐	0.50 ☐

Note 1. The 10 unit 'Cardphone' card, D1 below, was in fact mainly used as a complimentary but has been listed as a definitive since it clearly falls into the 'Cardphone' series. The unit was then 5

Note 2. A further printing of C1, after the printing of C2, has been reported but does not appear in Landis and Gyr's records and no copy of C1 dated after January, 1986, has been seen.

C3	*C3*	5	1/86	COMPANY MESSAGE, Green, blue / silver (5000)	60.00 ☐	30.00 ☐
C3(a)	*C3(a)*	5	1/86	COMPANY MESSAGE, Reverse as *C3(a)*, Six figure number at bottom right on front (v.rare)	--- ☐	--- ☐
C4	*C4*	5	9/87	LANDIS & GYR – 75 YRS, Green / silver (9000)	125.00 ☐	75.00 ☐
C5	*(C2)*	5	1/90	Green / silver, Notched (63,200)	1.00 ☐	0.50 ☐
C6	*C6*	3	9/90	Green, white / silver (500,000)	1.00 ☐	0.50 ☐
C7	*(C6)*	10	9/90	Green, white / silver (100,000)	1.50 ☐	0.50 ☐

Note. C3 was issued, initially at a conference in Brighton, as a sample to demonstrate the advertising potential. C3(a), which has only recently come to light, was from a very limited (perhaps as few as 12) printing trial for BT after the issue of C3 the telephone number on the reverse was then that of BT's marketing group. C3(a) may exist printed in gold (as above), silver or green on the reverse. C4 celebrated 75 years of Landis and Gyr's trading in the UK.

D – DEFINITIVE CARDS

First (Cardphone) Series.

D1	*D1*	10	1981	Green / silver (50,000)	150.00 ☐	30.00 ☐
D4	*(D1)*	40	7/81	Green / silver (2,635,000)	5.00 ☐	1.50 ☐
D5	*(D1)*	100	1983	Green / silver (552,000)	12.00 ☐	7.50 ☐
D6	*D6*	200	7/81	Green / silver (481,000)	24.00 ☐	6.00 ☐
D6(a)				Control on inverted card (incl. above)	150.00 ☐	60.00 ☐

Note 1. The 20 and 30 unit cardphone cards listed as D2 and D3 in an earlier book are no longer listed. Neither appears in the production records of Landis and Gyr although sample or trial copies of a 30 unit card certainly exist.

Note 2. In the case of D6(a) above and D11(a) below, the control has been applied to an inverted card, i.e. when the card is turned over like a page of a book, the number appears inverted in the top left corner of the reverse rather than the right way up in the bottom right corner as was usual at that time. Inverted controls are in the correct position at bottom right on the reverse but are upside down. Most UK cards over the last three years have had inverted controls due to a change in the control stamping wheels.

Note 3. A trial version of D5 with a 2mm white band over the optical strip is known to exist.

Second (Phonecard) Series - No notch.

No.	Ill.	Units	Date	Description		Value	
D7	*D7*	10	6/84	Green / silver (long track) (10,759,000)	2.50 ☐	0.50 ☐
D7(a)				(short track) (incl. above)	6.00 ☐	4.00 ☐
D8	*(D7)*	20	4/85	Green / silver (long track) (9,935,000)	3.50 ☐	0.60 ☐
D8(a)				(short track) (incl. above)	6.00 ☐	4.00 ☐
D8(b)				Control missing	-- ☐	-- ☐
D9	*(D7)*	40	6/84	Green / silver (short track) (7,638,000)	6.00 ☐	1.00 ☐
D10	*(D7)*	100	6/84	Green / silver (long track) (2,423,000)	15.00 ☐	2.50 ☐
D10(a)				(short track) (incl. above)	15.00 ☐	2.50 ☐
D11	*D11*	200	6/84	Green / silver (916,000)	25.00 ☐	5.00 ☐
D11(a)				Control on inverted card	40.00 ☐	10.00 ☐

Third (Notched) Series.

No.	Ill.	Units	Date	Description		Value	
D12	*(D7)*	10	10/87	Green / silver (??????)	1.20 ☐	0.30 ☐
D12(a)				Control **not** inverted	5.00 ☐	1.00 ☐
D12(b)				Control **missing**	-- ☐	75.00 ☐
D13	*(D7)*	20	10/87	Green / silver (??????)	2.40 ☐	0.60 ☐
D13(a)				Control **not** inverted	4.00 ☐	1.50 ☐
D13(b)				Control missing	-- ☐	20.00 ☐
D13(c)				Short track	-- ☐	--- ☐
D13A	*(D7)*	40	10/87	Green / silver (??????)	4.50 ☐	0.60 ☐
D13A(a)				Control **not** inverted	5.00 ☐	1.00 ☐
D13A(b)				Control missing	-- ☐	20.00 ☐
D13B	*(D7)*	100	10/87	Green / silver	12.00 ☐	2.00 ☐
D13B(a)				Control missing	-- ☐	30.00 ☐
D13C	*(D11)*	200	6/90	Green / silver (??????)	25.00 ☐	12.00 ☐
D13C(a)				Control on inverted card	100.00 ☐	50.00 ☐

Note. Inverted controls are usual for this series. Missing controls, which have now been found on all but the 200 of the above values, are very rare and are thought to be due to a machine malfunction. More generally Landis and Gyr cards without controls are often 'specimens' they may never have been encoded and may even have no optical strip at all. A few cases of two controls, side by side, on one card and a few double strikes have been reported.

Fourth Series.

No.	Ill.	Units	Date	Description		Value	
D14	*(D15)*	10	5/88	Green / silver (29,885)	50.00 ☐	15.00 ☐
D15	*D15*	20	5/88	Green / silver (29,179)	60.00 ☐	20.00 ☐
D16	*D16*	10	2/89	Green / silver (500,000)	5.00 ☐	2.00 ☐
D16(a)				Control **not** inverted (incl. above)	5.00 ☐	3.00 ☐

Note 1. D14 and D15 were trials for a new design and were manufactured in Switzerland. The control numbers on them are not inverted and do not follow the normal UK pattern. D16 was manufactured later, in the UK, and differs from D14 in the length of the word 'Phonecard' and, most noticeably, in that the horizontal line across the card is 2mm wide while those on D14 and D15 are 1mm wide its controls are normally inverted and of the usual UK type. It is relatively common.

Note 2. Two cards, similar to D13B but with a white band over the optical track, have been reported the status of these is unclear but they may have been engineering trial cards.

C1

C2

C3

C3(a)(reverse)

C4

C6

D1

D6

D7

D11

D15

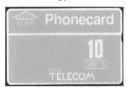

D16

D20

D24

D27

S3

S4

S5

S6

S7

S10

Fifth (Offset) Series.

No.	Ill.	Units	Date	Description	Value	
D17	*(D20)*	10	2/90	Green (shades), white / silver (1,179,600)	1.50 ☐	0.50 ☐
D17(a)				Control missing	-- ☐	75.00 ☐
D18	*(D20)*	20	2/90	Green (shades), white / silver (15,397,950)	2.50 ☐	0.50 ☐
D18(a)				Control missing	-- ☐	35.00 ☐
D19	*(D20)*	40	10/90	Green (shades), white / silver (4,088,900)	4.50 ☐	0.50 ☐
D19(a)				Control missing	-- ☐	25.00 ☐
D19(b)				Blue-green, white lines bordering gap	5.00 ☐	1.00 ☐
D20	*D20*	100	2/90	Green, white / silver (1,920,600)	11.00 ☐	1.00 ☐
D20(a)				Control missing	-- ☐	35.00 ☐
D20(b)				Blue-green, white lines bordering gap	13.00 ☐	2.00 ☐
D21	*(D20)*	200	12/90	Green, white / silver (135,231)	22.00 ☐	4.00 ☐

Note. This series is offset-printed apart from the green band over the optical strip which is silk-screened. The first copies to be found lacked controls and were probably engineering trial cards. The 40 and 100 unit cards occur in two forms, one yellowish green and one blue-green with very thin white lines above and below the (4.5mm) gap in the offset design. This gap can be 5mm or 5.5mm wide in the 20 and yellowish green 100 unit cards while the silk-screened band itself varies in width with 3.3, 3.7 and 4.0mm bands occurring. This is a complex series and more work on the permutations is nee

Sixth Series - 'Bonus' cards.

No.	Ill.	Units	Date	Description	Value	
D22	*(D24)*	20	1/ 10/90	Green, white / silver (100,000)	2.50 ☐	1.50 ☐
D23	*(D24)*	40+3	1/ 10/90	Green, white / silver (50,000)	5.00 ☐	2.00 ☐
D24	*D24*	100+10	1/ 10/90	Green, white / silver (25,000)	12.50 ☐	5.00 ☐

Note. The so-called 'bonus' cards were an experimental series which were released for a three month trial in the South Midlands. It was the first use in the UK of free added units on higher value cards to encourage the purchase of these although this is standard practice in other countries such as Belgium and the Netherlands. There is no bonus on the 20 unit card.

Seventh Series - New Logo.

No.	Ill.	Units	Date	Description	Value	
D25	*(D27)*	20	4/91	Green, white / silver	2.50 ☐	0.50 ☐
D26	*(D27)*	40	4/91	Green, white / silver	4.50 ☐	0.50 ☐
D27	*D27*	100	4/91	Green, white / silver	11.00 ☐	0.50 ☐
D27(a)				Control missing	-- ☐	-- ☐
D28	*(D27)*	200	4/91	Green, white / silver	22.00 ☐	3.00 ☐

Note. This new series was introduced in the context of a British Telecom publicity campaign launched on 20 March, 1991. No 10-unit (£1) cards are intended for this series.

S - SPECIAL/COMMEMORATIVE CARDS

No.	Ill.	Units	Date	Description	Value	
S1	*(S3)*	10	1/7/87	MUIRFIELD (GOLF), Green / silver (6000)	300.00 ☐	150.00 ☐
S2	*(S3)*	20	1/7/87	MUIRFIELD (GOLF), Green / silver (5000)	350.00 ☐	200.00 ☐
S3	*S3*	100	1/7/87	MUIRFIELD (GOLF), Green / silver (900)	1000.00 ☐	700.00 ☐
S4	*S4*	40	4/11/87	LONDON CHALLENGE, Black, white, green (500)	650.00 ☐	450.00 ☐

Note. The British Telecom London Challenge card was issued in connection with a joint initiative between British Telecom and the Student Industrial Society to promote the latter. Very few were sold on that occasion and others were disposed of in connection with Live Aid, a charity event.

No.	Ill.	Units	Date	Description	Value	
S5	*S5*	20	16/11/87	CHRISTMAS 1987, Multicolour (100,000)	6.00 ☐	4.00 ☐
S5(a)				Control inverted	4.00 ☐	3.00 ☐

Note. S5 was made in Switzerland.

No.	Ill.	Units	Date	Description	Value	
S6	*S6*	40	18/1/88	VALENTINE'S DAY 1988, Multicolour (250,000)	7.00 ☐	4.00 ☐
S6(a)				Control missing	-- ☐	-- ☐
S7	*S7*	20	7/88	EDINBURGH FESTIVAL 1988, Multicolour (30,000)	40.00 ☐	25.00 ☐
S8	*(S7)*	40	7/88	EDINBURGH FESTIVAL 1988, Multicolour (15,000)	15.00 ☐	8.00 ☐
S9	*(S7)*	100	7/88	EDINBURGH FESTIVAL 1988, Multicolour (8,000)	15.00 ☐	10.00 ☐

No.	Ill.	Units	Date	Description		Value	
S10	*S10*	40	10/88	FIFTY MILLIONTH, Blue, green / gold (600)	800.00 ☐	500.00 ☐

Note. This rare card commemorated the production of 50,000,000 Landis and Gyr cards in the UK. They were given to BT officials and journalists at the celebration. About half were in leather wallets.

No.	Ill.	Units	Date	Description		Value	
S11	*S11*	20	10/88	CHRISTMAS 1988, Multicolour (1,500,700)	6.00 ☐	2.00 ☐
S11(a)				Deeper shade of blue	8.00 ☐	3.00 ☐
S11(b)				Control missing	-- ☐	50.00 ☐
S12	*S12*	40	10/88	CHRISTMAS 1988, Multicolour (750,000)	5.00 ☐	2.00 ☐
S12(a)				Control inverted	5.00 ☐	2.00 ☐
S12(b)				Control missing	-- ☐	-- ☐

Note. S11 was manufactured in the UK. The two shades of blue background are quite distinct and are accompanied by different shades of green. S12 was manufactured in Switzerland.

No.	Ill.	Units	Date	Description		Value	
S13	*S13*	20	10/89	WINTER 1989, Multicolour (1,224,400)	3.00 ☐	0.50 ☐
S13(a)				Short track	-- ☐	-- ☐
S13(b)				Control missing	-- ☐	75.00 ☐
S14	*S14*	40	10/89	WINTER 1989, Multicolour (365,800)	5.00 ☐	1.00 ☐
S14(a)				Control not inverted	5.00 ☐	1.00 ☐
S14(b)				Control missing	-- ☐	40.00 ☐
S15	*S15*	100	10/89	WINTER 1989, Multicolour (151,000)	12.00 ☐	3.00 ☐
S15(a)				Control not inverted	-- ☐	75.00 ☐
S15(b)				Control missing	-- ☐	30.00 ☐

Note. 600 of S14 and 600 of D15 were manufactured in Switzerland. These can in theory be distinguished by the presence of ridges above and below the optical track on UK-made cards and their absence on Swiss-made cards. There are marked differences in shade in the two lower values the blue being much stronger in some than in others. There are also differences in the surface textures. Some copies of D15 have the 'British / TELECOM' offset on the reverse. Cards with 999 (followed by a letter) controls can be found for all three values. These are short-run cards made to make up for any rejected cards in a batch or, if Type 4, proofs and are rare.

No.	Ill.	Units	Date	Description		Value	
S16	*S16*	20	2/90	FORTH BRIDGE CENTENARY, Multicolour (50,000)	4.50 ☐	1.50 ☐
S17	*S17*	40	2/90	FORTH BRIDGE CENTENARY, Multicolour (25,000)	6.00 ☐	2.50 ☐
S18	*S18*	20	4/90	GLASGOW 1990, Multicolour (74,800)	3.00 ☐	1.50 ☐
S19	*(S18)*	40	4/90	GLASGOW 1990, Multicolour (35,200)	5.00 ☐	2.50 ☐
S20	*S20*	20	4/90	GATESHEAD GARDEN FESTIVAL, Multicolour (50,400)	3.00 ☐	2.00 ☐
S21	*S21*	40	4/90	GATESHEAD GARDEN FESTIVAL, Multicolour (28,800)	5.00 ☐	3.00 ☐
S22	*S22*	20	4/90	SPRING 1990, Multicolour (1,036,400)	3.00 ☐	1.00 ☐
S22(a)				Control missing	-- ☐	60.00 ☐
S23	*S23*	40	4/90	SPRING 1990, Multicolour (474,000)	5.00 ☐	2.00 ☐
S23(a)				Control missing	-- ☐	75.00 ☐
S24	*S24*	100	4/90	SPRING 1990, Multicolour (184,400)	12.00 ☐	4.00 ☐
S24(a)				Control missing	-- ☐	50.00 ☐
S25	*S25*	20	5/90	MANCHESTER OLYMPIC BID, Multicolour (120,000)	3.00 ☐	2.00 ☐
S26	*S26*	40	5/90	MANCHESTER OLYMPIC BID, Multicolour (59,600)	5.00 ☐	3.00 ☐
S27	*S27*	20	6/90	WIMBLEDON TENNIS, Multicolour (23,200)	3.00 ☐	2.00 ☐
S28	*S28*	20	7/90	BRITISH WILDLIFE APPEAL, Multicolour (1,894,200)	3.00 ☐	0.50 ☐
S28(a)				Control missing	-- ☐	60.00 ☐
S29	*S29*	40	7/90	BRITISH WILDLIFE APPEAL, Multicolour (793,400)	5.00 ☐	1.00 ☐
S29(a)				Control missing	-- ☐	75.00 ☐
S30	*S30*	100	7/90	BRITISH WILDLIFE APPEAL, Multicolour (185,200)	12.00 ☐	2.00 ☐
S30(a)				Control missing	-- ☐	50.00 ☐

S11

S12

S13

S14

S15

S16

S17

S18

S20

S21

S22

S23

S24

S25

S26

S27

S28

S29

S30

S31

S32

S33

S34

S35

S36

S37

S38

S39

GENERAL NOTE. Landis and Gyr cards can also occasionally be found as 'specimens' or 'proofs'. Specimens generally have no optical strip below the band and are thus not encoded. Proofs are the first production cards sent to the customer for approval and do normally have an optical strip but they usually have a special control number – often with the 999 prefix used for short production runs. Recent proofs seen have 999A... prefixes in the rare Type 4 font (page 18).

No.	Ill.	Units	Date	Description	Value	
S31	*S31*	20	10/90	WINTER 1990, Multicolour (2,014,000)	3.00 ☐	0.50 ☐
S31(a)				Control missing	-- ☐	60.00 ☐
S32	*S32*	40	10/90	WINTER 1990, Multicolour (682,400)	5.00 ☐	1.00 ☐
S32(a)				Control missing	-- ☐	75.00 ☐
S32(b)				Control on inverted card	-- ☐	-- ☐
S33	*S33*	100	10/90	WINTER 1990, Multicolour (197,200)	12.00 ☐	2.00 ☐
S33(b)				Control missing	-- ☐	40.00 ☐
S34	*S34*	20	11/90	100,000,000th, Blue, yellow, green (5000)	12.00 ☐	6.00 ☐
S35	*S35*	40	1/91	INTERCITY RAIL, Multicolour (64,500)	5.00 ☐	1.50 ☐
S36	*S36*	10	3/91	CITY OF LONDON, Multicolour (15,000)	2.00 ☐	2.00 ☐
S37	*S37*	10	3/91	EAST ANGLIA, Multicolour (15,000)	2.00 ☐	2.00 ☐
S38	*S38*	10	3/91	SEVERNSIDE, Multicolour (15,000)	2.00 ☐	2.00 ☐

Note. S36, 37 and 38 represent British Telecom districts and the cards are refered to within BT as 'District Cards'.

S39	*S39*	20	3/91	BELFAST UNIVERSITY, Multicolour (5,000)	5.00 ☐	3.00 ☐
S40	---	20	4/91	BIRMINGHAM INTERNAT. CENTRE, Multicol. (50,000)	3.00 ☐	2.00 ☐

A - ADVERTISING CARDS

A1	*A1*	10	1/12/86	GRAHAM'S WHISKY, Black, red, green (15,000)	125.00 ☐	60.00 ☐

Note. A1 has been reported with three different widths of strip (*not* band) as seen in the margins at the end of the green band - 3.2mm, 3.6mm and 4.2mm. These seem to be about equally common.

A2	*A2*	10	1987	MENTADENT, Multicolour (Swiss-made) (50,000)	50.00 ☐	15.00 ☐
A2A	*(A2)*	10	1988	MENTADENT, Notch added (Swiss-made) (60,000)	5.00 ☐	3.00 ☐
A2A(a)				Control not inverted	5.00 ☐	5.00 ☐
A3	*A3*	10	1987	TREBOR, Green / silver (26,700)	80.00 ☐	35.00 ☐
A3(a)				Control missing	-- ☐	-- ☐
A4	*A4*	10	11/87	BIRD'S, Green / silver (5000)	50.00 ☐	25.00 ☐
A4(a)				Control missing	-- ☐	-- ☐
A5	*A5*	10	2/88	GATEWAY, Black, green / silver (30,000)	40.00 ☐	20.00 ☐
A6	*A6*	5	3/88	PERSIL, Multicolour (630,990)	3.00 ☐	2.00 ☐
A6(a)				Darker blue	6.00 ☐	4.00 ☐

Note. A version of A6 without the white box round the logo exists as a specimen and a few may have been issued. A6, even when sealed, often has a scrape in the margin by the 'd' in Phonecard. The variety A6(a) with a non-inverted control reported in 'The Stanley Gibbons Catalogue of Telephone Cards', 2nd edition, does not appear to exist.

A7	*A7*	5	3/88	BROOKE BOND,Yellow, red, green/silver (250,000)	50.00 ☐	5.00 ☐
A7(a)				Control not inverted	50.00 ☐	5.00 ☐
A8	*A8*	10	3/88	BROOKE BOND,Yellow, red, green/silver (45,550)	25.00 ☐	15.00 ☐
A8(a)				Control not inverted	35.00 ☐	15.00 ☐

Note. A7 and A8 were manufactured in Switzerland. A7 shows two distinct shades of red and a tendency to colour misplacement of either red or yellow.

A9	*A9*	10	4/88	PALMOLIVE, Blue, white, magenta / silver (30,000)	2.50 ☐	1.50 ☐
A9(a)				Control missing	-- ☐	-- ☐

No.	Ill.	Units	Date	Description		Value	
A10	*A10*	10	5/88	CASTLEMAINE, Multicolour (20,000)		15.00 ☐	12.00 ☐
A10(a)				Control missing		-- ☐	-- ☐
A11	*A11*	40	5/88	.. .. (10,000)		25.00 ☐	20.00 ☐
A12	*A12*	20	7/88	GLAXO, Blue, green / silver (52,600)		75.00 ☐	10.00 ☐
A13	*A13*	40	8/88	3i, Blue, black, yellow, green / silver (5500)		250.00 ☐	150.00 ☐
A13(a)				Control missing		-- ☐	-- ☐
A14	*A14*	10	10/89	LANDIS & GYR - DFS, Green / silver (400)		350.00 ☐	200.00 ☐
A15	*(A14)*	40	10/89	LANDIS & GYR - DFS, Green / silver (50)		1200.00 ☐	750.00 ☐
A16	*A16*	20	11/89	WILTSHIER, Blue,red,white,green/silver (11,100)		25.00 ☐	15.00 ☐
A17	*A17*	5	11/89	SIGMAGYR, Multicolour (5,000)		75.00 ☐	40.00 ☐
A18	*A18*	10	5/90	CASTROL GTX, Green, white, red, black (108,000)		8.00 ☐	3.00 ☐
A19	*A19*	20	12/90	HORLICKS, Multicolour (30,000)		3.00 ☐	2.00 ☐
A20	*A20*	100	2/91	AMERICAN EXPRESS, Multicolour (10,000)		15.00 ☐	5.00 ☐
A21	*A21*	20	1/91	TEXAS HOMECARE, Multicolour (50,000)		3.00 ☐	3.00 ☐
A22	*A22*	10	3/91	SAINSBURY'S, Green and white (10,000)		2.00 ☐	1.50 ☐
A23	---	5	4/91	KITE PROMOTION, Multicolour (4650)		3.00 ☐	2.00 ☐
A24	---	20	4/91	HILTON, Multicolour (24,000)		3.00 ☐	2.00 ☐

Note. The Sainsbury card, A22, was overprinted by Sainsbury's onto the 10-unit complimentary card, C7, and the old design can just be seen below if the card is held at the right angle.

O - OFFICIAL/SERVICE CARDS

No.	Ill.	Units	Date	Description		Value	
O1	*O1*	(200)	1983?	Green / silver (short track)		---	75.00 ☐
O2	*(O1)*	(200)	1986?	Green / silver (long track)		---	15.00 ☐
O3	*(O1)*	(200)	1989	Green / silver - Notched		---	10.00 ☐
O3(a)				Control on inverted card		---	10.00 ☐

T - TEST CARDS

No.	Ill.	Units	Date	Description		Value	
T1	*T1*	-	1983?	Green / silver		---	400.00 ☐
T2	*(T3)*	-	?	Green / matt silver		---	150.00 ☐
T3	*T3*	-	?	Green / polished silver		---	50.00 ☐
T3(a)	*(T3)*			Three numbers across upper line		---	50.00 ☐
T4	*T4*	-	1990	Green / polished silver		---	25.00 ☐

Note. The printed numbers on T2 and T3 and the manuscript numbers on T1 refer to settings of the telephones being tested and differ from card to card. Like the Service cards they are not available to the general public in an unused condition and no unused price is therefore given.

General Note: In addition to the above, there exist a number of private cards, essentially visiting cards, bearing the names of specific individuals. These are not generally available and are not therefore listed.

A1

A2

A3

A4

A5

A6

A7

A8

A9

A10

A11

A12

A13

A14

A16

A17

A18

A19

A20

A21

A22

01

T1

T4

GREAT BRITAIN - BRITISH TELECOM

CONTROL NUMBERS ON BRITISH TELECOM CARDS

Many collectors in the UK enjoy the study and collecting of the many different control number types impressed into the backs of Landis and Gyr cards. As explained in the introduction to the British Telecom section, batches of cards, usually of 100,000, have a common prefix of the type XYYZ..... where X is the last digit of the year of manufacture, e.g. 7 for 1987 or 0 for 1990, YY is the month of manufacture, e.g. 12 for December or 06 for June, and Z is a letter. The first month digit is often higher than 0 or 1 but all even numbers equate to 0 and all odd numbers equate to 1 so that 01=21=41=61=81=January. The five figures following are a simple serial control number from 00000 to 99999. The two extreme numbers are greatly prized. Below are listed all reported control prefixes for all issued BT cards. For large issue cards each prefix will usually represent 100,000 cards but sometimes one batch which was not completed will be rare. It should be remembered however that cards are distributed all over the UK and the prefix which seems to be rare in London may be common in Belfast or Glasgow. Sometimes the prefix 999 is used for a few cards made separately to complete a batch, to replace defective cards or as proofs these are rare. The earliest cards were made in Switzerland and have controls of a different type, some with simple numbers but most with the letter G (for Great Britain) followed by a digit and a letter. To save space the prefixes listed below are given in condensed form - thus '502A,B,C,D' means that prefixes known are 502A.., 502B.., 502C.. and 502D... If the numbers appear to be the right way up in the bottom right corner on the reverse of the card when the card is turned over through a vertical axis like the page of a book, the number is said to be "normal". If the number appears to be upside down it is said to be "inverted". (I) means that the numbers following it are inverted. No indication or an (N) means that they are normal. Controls on BT cards are found in five different fonts (shapes and sizes of characters) These are known as Type 1 (T1) to Type 5 (T5) and are indicated in the listings below. The actual fonts are as follows:

Type 1. (T1) 1 2 3 4 5 6 7 8 9 0   2.1 mm. Also known inverted but very rare

Type 2. (T2) 1 2 3 4 5 6 7 8 9 0   2.1 mm.

Type 3. (T3) 1 2 3 4 5 6 7 8 9 0   2.1 mm.

Type 4. (T4) 1 2 3 4 5 6 7 8 9 0   2.0 mm. Normally in groups of three characters.

Type 5. (T5) 1 2 3 4 5 6 7 8 9 0   2.2 mm. Similar to (T3). Control 2 mm longer.

COMPLIMENTARY CARDS

C1 - (T1) (T2) 001H. 511A,B. 512A,B,C,D. 601A,B,C,D,E,F,G,H. 601F on inverted card.
C2 - (T1) (T2) 601H. 602A,B,C,D,E,F,G,H,K. 603A,B,C,D,E,F,G,H,K. 604A,B,C,D,E,F,G,H.
605A,B. 606B. 607A. 608B. 609C. 610D. 611E. 612F.
C3 - (T1) 511B,D.   C4 - (T1) 708A   C5 - (I) (T3) 932H. 004A.
C6 - (I) (T3) (T5) 050D,E,F,G,H. 070B,C.   C7 - (I) (T3) (T5) 070K. 090F,K.

DEFINITIVE CARDS

D1 - (T1) 6 digits. G4+6 digits. 403A. 406A.
D4 - (T1) (T2) (T4) 6 digits. G0+6 digits. G1+6 digits. G6+6 digits. 403A,B,C,D.
404E,S,T,U,W. 405C,F,G,H,K,L. 406A,B,C,E. 408A,B. 409B
D5 - (T1) (T2) G5+6 digits. 403A,B. 404C,D,E. 405E,F. 406C. 407D. 408A.
D6 - (T1) 2 digits. 3 digits. 6 digits. G2+6 digits. G2+6 digits on inverted card.
403A. 404B. 405C. 406D. 408A. Also 403A, 405C, 406D on inverted card.

D7 - (T1) (T4) (Short track) 406A,B. 505A. 506A. 507A. 508A. 512B,C,D. 601C. 605K.
(Long track) 512B,C,D. 601C,D,E,F. 602C,D,E,F,G. 603D,E,F,G,H. 604S,T,U,V. 605F,G,H,K.
606F,G,K,L. 607A,G,H,K,L,N. 608F,G,H,K,L. 609F,G,H,K,L. 610A,B,C,D,E. 611A,B,C,D,E.
612A,B,C,D,E. 701A,B,C,D,E. 702A,B,C,D,E. 703A,B,C,D,E. 704A,B,C,D,E. 705A,B,C,D,E.
706A,B,C,D,E. 707A,B,C,D,E. 708A,B,C,D,E. 709A,B,C,D,E.
D8 - (T1) (T4) (Short track) 503A,B. 504C,D. 505B,C,D. 506B. 507B. 508B,C. 509A,B.
510A,B. 511A,B,C. 512A. 601A. 602B. 603A. 607M. (Long track) 510A,B. 511A,B,C.
601A,B. 602A,B,C. 603A,B,C. 604A,B,C,D,E. 605A,B,C,D,E. 606A,B,C,D,E.
607B,C,D,E,F,M. 608A,B,C,D,E. 609A,B,C,D,E. 610F,G,H,K,L. 611F,G,H,S. 612F,G,H,K,L.
721A,B,C,D,E. 722A,B,C,D. 723A,B,C,D,E. 724A,B,C,D. 725A,B,C,D. 726A,B,C,D.
727A,B,C,D. 728A,B,C,D. 729A,B. Control missing.
D9 - (T1) (T2) 406A,B,C,D,E. 407A,B,C,D. 408B,C,D,E. 409A,C,D,E. 410A,B,C,D,E,F,G.
411A,B,C,D,E,F,G. 412A,B,C,D,E,F. 501A,B,C,D,E,F,G. 502A,B,C,D,E,F,G. 503A,B,C,D.
D10 - (T1) (T4) (Short track) 406C,D. 407D. 408F. 409F. 410F,G. 411A,B. 412A,B.
501A,B,C. 502A,B,C. 503A,B. (Long track) 610M,N. 612M,N. 702M,N. 724E. 725E.
726E. 727E. 728E. 729D,E.
D11 - (T1) 406D. 407E. 408T. 409T. 410T. 411A. 412A. 502B. 503C. Also 406D. 407E. 408T.
409T. 412A. 502B. 503C. on inverted card.

D12 - (N) (T1) 710A,B,C,D,E. 730E. 711A,B,C,D,E. 721D,E. 731D,E. 712A,B,C,D,E. 732B,D,E.
801A,B,C,D,E,F. 821D,E. 802A,B,C,D,E. 822D,E. 803A,B,C,D. 810C. 811H.
891A,B,C,D,E,F. 892A. 941B,C. 981A,D,E,F,G,H. 982A,B. 948A,D. 988C,D. 999B.

(I) *(T3) (T4) (T5)* 712B. 803C,E. 823E. 804A,B,C,D,E,F,G,H,K,L. 824A,L.
805A,B,C,D,E,F,G,H,K,L. 806A,B,C,D,E,F,G,H,K,L. 826K. 807A,B,C,D,E,F,G,H. 827G.
808A,B,C,D,E,F,G. 809A,B,C,D,E,F. 810A,B,C,D,E,F. 850A. 811A,B,F,G,H. 851B,C.
891A,B. 852B,C. 892B,C,D,E. 901A,B. 941B,C. 981A. 902F,G,H,K. 982B,C,D. 904A.
905A,B,C,D,E. 906B,C,D,E,F,G,H. 907E,F,G,H,K. 927A,B,C,D,E. 928E,F,G,H,K. 948B,C.
988A,B,D,E. 909E. 929D. 910A,B,H,K. 930A,B,C,D,E. 911A,B,C,D,E,F,G,H. 941B,C.
912A,B,C,D,F,G,H. 001A,B,C,D,E. 051A,B,C,D. 003D,E,F. 063B. 004F. 025H. 045H,K.
006A,B,C,D,E. Control missing
D13 - (N) *(T1)* 729C,D. 730A,B,C,D. 731A,B,C. 732A,B,C. 821A,B,C. 822A,B,C. 823A,B,C.
(I) *(T3) (T4)* 747B. 841D. 823D. 827A,B,C,D,E. 828A,B,C,D. 830G,H,K. 831A,B,C,D.
871A,C,D,E,F,G,H,K. 812A,B,C,D,E,F,G,H. 901H,K. 921A,B,C,D,E,F,G,H,K. 922A,B,C,D.
942A,B. 903F,G,H,K. 923A,B,C,D,E,F,G,H,K. 943A. 904E,F,G,H,K. 924G,H,K.
944A,B,C,D,E,F. 905G,H,K. 925A,B,C,D,E,F,G,H,K. 945A,B,C. 906K. 926A,B,C,D,E,F,G,H,K.
946A,B,C,D. 927F,G,H,K. 947A,B,C,D,E,F,G. 909G,H,K. 950A,B,C. 930F,G,H,K. 911K.
931A,B,C,D,E,F,G. 912K. 932B. 021A,D,F. 061C,D. 081D. 023D,G,K. 043E. 999B.
Control missing.
D13A- (N) *(T1)* 985A,B,C. 951F.
(I) *(T3) (T4)* 901C,D,E,F. 941A. 902B,C,D,E. 922G,H,K. 903B,C,D,E. 943B,C,D,E,F.
924A,B,C,D,E,F,G. 944G. 945D. 985A,B,C. 946E. 907B,C,D. 910D,E,F,G. 931H,K.
951C,H. 041A. 061B. 022K. 043D,E,F,G. 026D,E,F. 066H. 999B. Control missing.
D13B- (I) *(T3) (T4)* 850B,C,E. 851A. 852A. 901G. 902A. 922E,F. 903A. 904C. 905F. 906A.
907A. 909A,B,C. 950D. 951D,E. 041E,G,H. 042A. 043A. Control missing.
D13C- (I) *(T5)* 005E. Also 005E. on inverted card.

D14 - (I) *(T3)* 803E.   D15 - (I) *(T3)* 823D.
D16 - (N) *(T1)* 847A,B. 848A,C. 850B,C,E. 811D.
(I) *(T3)* 848B,C. 810E. 850A,B,C,D,E. 811C.

D17 - (I) *(T3) (T4)* 001F,G. 061F. 003A,B,C. 063A. 004A,B,C,E. 045G. Control missing.
D18 - (I) *(T3) (T4) (T5)* 932A. 001F,G,H,K. 021B,C,E. 061E,G,K. 042E. 003G,H,K.
023A,B,C,D,E,F,H. 004G,H,K. 024A,B,C,D,E,F,G,K. 005F,G,H,K. 025A,B,D,E,F,K. 045A.
066F. 007A,B. 027A,B,C,D,E,F,G,H,K. 047A,B,D,E,F,G. 067B,C,D,E,F,G,H. 008A,B,F,H.
068A,F,H. 068D. 070F,G,H,K. 999B,C. Control missing.
D19 - (I) *(T3) (T5)* 044F,G. 005A. 086A,B. 087B. 048H,K. 068A,B. 090E,G. Control missing.
D20 - (I) *(T3) (T4) (T5)* 912E. 041F. 042D. 043K. 044B,K. 066K. 086C,H,K. 048A. 999C.
Control missing.
D21 - (I) *(T5)* 010A.

D22 - (I) *(T3)* 030C,D,E,F, G.   D23 - (I) *(T3)* 010F,G,H. 011E.   D24 - (I) *(T3)* 010E.

S1 - (N) *(T1)* 747A. S2 - (N) *(T1)* 747B. S3 - (N) *(T1)* 747C. S4 - (N) *(T1)* 747E.
S5 - (N) *(T1)* 711A. 712B.   S6 - (N) *(T1)* 752A,B,C.   S7 - (I) *(T3)* 747B.
S8 - (I) *(T3)* 752C.   S9 - (T3) (I) 747C.   S10 - (T3) (I) 999B.
S11 - (I) *(T3)* 829A,B,C,D,E,F,G,H,K. 830A,B,C,D,E,F. 871A,B? Control missing.
S12 - (I) *(T3)* 809B,C,D. 810A,C,D,E. 831A,B,C.
(N) *(T1) (T2)* 809B,D. 810A,B,C,D,E,F. 811E. 831A,B,C. Control missing.
S13 - (I) *(T3) (T4)* 947H. 908A,B,D,E,F,G,H,K. 928A,B,C,D. 909F. 919A. 999B.
(N) *(T1)* 908 C. Control missing. (I) (Short track) 908B.
S14 - (I) *(T3)* 986A,B,C. 948E. 929A,B,C. 950G. 999B. (N) *(T1)* 986A,B C. Control missing.
S15 - (I) *(T3)* 909D,E. 919B. Control missing. (N) 985G. S16 - (I) *(T3)* 021K.
S17 - (I) *(T3)* 041D.   S18 - (I) *(T3)* 021H.
S19 - (I) *(T3)* 041B.   S20 - (I) *(T3)* 021G. 999G.   S21 - (I) *(T3)* 041C.
S22 - (I) *(T3) (T4)* 002A,B,C,D,E,F,G,H,K. 022A,B. 042C. Control missing.
S23 - (I) *(T3)* 002D. 022C,D,E,F. Control missing.   S24 - (I) *(T3)* 022G,H. Control missing.
S25 - (I) *(T3) (T4)* 043A,B.   S26 - (I) *(T3)* 043C.   S27 - (I) *(T3)* 025C. Control missing.
S28 - (I) *(T3) (T4)* 045B,C,D,E,F,G,H,K. 006G,H,K. 026A,B,C. 046B,C,D,E,F,G,H,K. 086G.
Control missing.
S29 - (I) *(T3) (T4)* 026G,H,K. 046A. 066A,BC,D. 007A,B. 999B. Control missing.
S30 - (I) *(T3)* 066D,E. No control.
S31 - (I) *(T3) (T4)* 009A,B,C,D,E,F. 029F,G H. 049A,B,D,E,F,K. 069A,B. 010B,C,D. 030A,B,H,K.
050A,B. 999C. Control missing.
S32 - (I) *(T3) (T5)* 009H,K. 029A,B,C,D,E,F. 049D, E, F. Control missing.
S33 - (I) *(T3) (T5)* 029C 999C. Control missing. S34 - (I) *(T3)* 009C. S35 - (I) *(T3)* 012D.

A1 - (N) *(T1)* 610S. A2 - (N) *(T1)* 704A. 712C. 802B?,D.   A2A - (N) *(T1)* 802D. 804B.
(I) *(T3)* 802D. A3 - (N) *(T1)* 747E. A4 - (N) *(T1)* 747E. Control missing.
A5 - (N) *(T1)* 747E.   A6 - (I) *(T3)* 747D. 708A. 861A,B,C,D. 862A,B,C,D.
A7 - (N) *(T1)* 801A,B,C. (I) *(T3)* 801A,B,C.   A8 - (N) *(T1)* 808A. (I) *(T3)* 801C,D.
A9 - (I) *(T3)* 824A. Control missing. A10 - (I) *(T3)* 747A. A11 - (I) *(T3)* 752C. Control
missing. A12 - (N) *(T1)* 807C. A13 - (I) *(T3)* 808H. Control missing.
A14 - (I) *(T3)* 945E.   A15 - (I) *(T3)* 946G. A16 - (I) *(T3)* 951G.   A17 - (N) *(T1)* 910B.
A18 - (I) *(T3)* 042B,F. A19 - (I) *(T3)* 009G. A20 - (I) 121C. A21 - (I) 161A. A22 - (I) 124K.

O1 - 6 or 8 digits. O2 - (N) *(T1)(T2)* 411S. 502S. 704S. 705S. 802S. 806S.
O3 - (N) 903S. (I) 009G. T1 - 8 digit number. Later test cards have no controls.

Discover the treasures of the Caribbean

MERCURY COMMUNICATIONS

Mercury Communications Ltd launched its payphone operations on 27 July, 1988, with the opening of 26 call boxes at Waterloo Station in London. The service has since spread throughout London and to other cities and towns in the UK. Cards are denominated in UK currency rather than units. Earlier cards have almost invisible control numbers on the reverse while many of the more recent cards have black controls against a white background. The latest cards no longer have the two ferrite strips in the top corners on the reverse but have a small 'C' at top right. The cards are manufactured by GPT, previously Plessey, UK, and are prefixed 'M' in the listings below. At the time of writing it is not possible to distinguish used from unused cards so in most cases only a single collectors' value is given. Mercury cards are classified as Definitives and Specials (both on sale generally) and Private issues which include advertising cards and other very limited issues not sold generally although all are on sale through Stanley Gibbons for the Mercury Collectors Club. Also listed is an 'Internal' card produced for Mercury for its own internal purposes and not issued to the public through any official channel. As with British Telecom, there also exist internal telephone cards in the form of visiting cards bearing the names of particular individuals but these are not listed. Paytelco is a joint company involving both GPT and Mercury which issues cards through multiple-site organisations such as chain stores, garages, hotels and so on. They have recently reached agreement with the Football Leagues of England and Scotland to issue cards at League club grounds. Paytelco cards are listed separately. Most Mercury and Paytelco cards exhibit shade variations and these are only mentioned where significant.

MC1	MC2	MC3
MD3	MS1	MS2
MS3	MS4	MS5
MS6	MS7	MS8
MS9	MS10	MS11

C - COMPLIMENTARY CARDS

No.	Ill.	Units	Date	Description	Value
MC1	*MC1*	(£0.40)	27/7/88	Silver, shades of metallic grey (27,000) '2MERA...'	15.00 □
MC1(a)				(incl. above) '3MERA...'	15.00 □
MC1(b)				(incl. above) '6MERA...'	10.00 □
MC2	*MC2*	(£0.40)	6/89	Multicolour (100,000) Control '12MERA...' at bottom	3.00 □
MC2(a)				(incl. above) Control '12MERA...' at top	4.00 □
MC3	*MC3*	(£0.40)	8/90	Multicolour (100,000) Control '21MERA...'	1.00 □

MD - DEFINITIVE CARDS

No.	Ill.	Units	Date	Description	Value
MD1	*(MD3)*	£2	27/7/88	Shades of metallic bronze (130,000) '2MERB...'	7.00 □
MD1(a)				(incl. above) '3MERB...'	5.00 □
MD1(b)				(incl. above) '7MERB...'	2.50 □
MD1(c)				Shades of metallic copper (incl. above) '6MERB...'	2.50 □
MD2	*(MD3)*	£4	27/7/88	Shades of metallic silver (38,185) '2MERC...'	8.00 □
MD2(a)				(incl. above) '7MERC...'	5.00 □
MD3	*MD3*	£10	27/7/88	Shades of metallic gold (14,000) '2MERD...'	25.00 □
MD3(a)				(incl. above) '6MERD...'	20.00 □

MS - SPECIAL / COMMEMORATIVE CARDS

No.	Ill.	Units	Date	Description	Value
MS1	*MS1*	£2	27/7/88	FIRST ISSUE, Multicoloured (5000) '1MERA...'	125.00 □
MS1(a)				(incl. above) '4MERA...'	100.00 □
MS1(b)				(incl. above) '5MERA...'	80.00 □
MS2	*MS2*	£4	27/7/88	FIRST ISSUE, Multicoloured (5000) '1MERB...'	20.00 □
MS2(a)				(incl. above) '4MERB...'	15.00 □
MS2(b)				(incl. above) '5MERB...'	6.00 □
MS3	*MS3*	£10	27/7/88	FIRST ISSUE, Multicoloured (5000) '1MERC...'	35.00 □
MS3(a)				(incl. above) '4MERC...'	30.00 □
MS3(b)				(incl. above) '5MERC...'	25.00 □
MS4	*MS4*	£5	9/88	WATERLOO CARD, Multicoloured (15,000) '7MERA...'	10.00 □
MS5	*MS5*	£2	10/88	CHRISTMAS 1988, Multicoloured (85,000) '8MERA...'	3.00 □
MS6	*MS6*	£4	10/88	CHRISTMAS 1988, Multicoloured (34,000) '8MERB...'	6.00 □
MS7	*MS7*	£10	10/88	CHRISTMAS 1988, Multicoloured (15,000) '8MERC...'	15.00 □
MS8	*MS8*	£2	5/89	LONDON, Multicoloured (19,459) '9MERA...'	2.50 □
MS9	*MS9*	£4	5/89	LONDON, Multicoloured (31,031) '9MERB...'	5.00 □
MS9(a)				(incl. above) '11MERB...'	15.00 □
MS10	*MS10*	£10	5/88	LONDON, Multicoloured (6000) '9MERC...'	35.00 □
MS11	*MS11*	£5	6/89	BIRMINGHAM, Multicoloured (5000) Control '8MERC...'	8.00 □
MS12	*MS12*	£5	6/89	BRISTOL, ... (5000) Control '8MERE...'	8.00 □
MS13	*MS13*	£5	6/89	EDINBURGH, ... (5000) Control '8MERA...'	8.00 □
MS14	*MS14*	£5	6/89	MANCHESTER, ... (5000) Control '8MERD...'	8.00 □
MS15	*MS15*	£5	6/89	GLASGOW TOWN HALL, .. (5000) Control '8MERB...'	8.00 □

Note. MS11 to MS15 were issued to mark the introduction of Mercury payphones in the named cities. MS15 was inscribed "Glasgow Town Hall" instead of 'Glasgow City Chambers' in error. The London cards, MS8 and MS9, later appeared with 'SPRING 1989' omitted - see MS23 and MS24.

No.	Ill.	Units	Date	Description	Value
MS16	*MS16*	£2	11/89	ALADDIN. CHRISTMAS 1989, Multicol.(20,000) '12MERA..'	3.00 □
MS17	*MS17*	£2	11/89	CINDERELLA. CHRISTMAS 1989, Multicol.(20,000) '12MERB..'	3.00 □
MS18	*MS18*	£2	11/89	BEANSTALK. CHRISTMAS 1989, Multicol.(20,000) '12MERC..'	3.00 □
MS19	*MS19*	£2	11/89	PUSS-IN-BOOTS CHRISTMAS 1989, Multicol.(20,000) '12MERD..'	3.00 □
MS20	*MS20*	£4	11/89	WHITTINGTON. CHRISTMAS 1989, Multicol.(20,000) '12MERE..'	6.00 □
MS21	*MS21*	£2	2/90	MAP OF UNDERGROUND, Multicoloured (19,459) '1MDCC...'	6.00 □
MS21(a)				MAP OF UNDERGROUND, Multicoloured (incl. above) '17MERE...'	10.00 □
MS21(b)				MAP OF UNDERGROUND, Multicoloured (incl. above) '18MERA...'	2.50 □
MS22	*MS22*	£2	7/90	MAP OF UNDERGROUND, Multicoloured (49,950) '23MERA...'/W	2.50 □

Note. The control on MS22 is black on a white background indicated here and elsewhere by '/W'. The designs on MS21 and MS22 differ in minor details. A third version is in preparation.

No.	Ill.	Units	Date	Description		Value
MS23	*(MS8)*	£2	5/90	LONDON, Multicoloured	(741,500) '9MERA...'	5.00 ☐
MS23(a)					(incl. above) '10MERA...'	2.50 ☐
MS24	*(MS9)*	£4	5/90	LONDON, Multicoloured	(31,031) '9MERB...'	5.00 ☐
MS24(a)					(incl. above) '11MERB...'	5.00 ☐

Note. MS23 and MS24 are similar to MS8 and MS9 but do not have 'SPRING 1989' in the bottom right corner.

No.	Ill.	Units	Date	Description		Value
MS25	*MS25*	£2	8/90	COLOURFUL WAY TO CALL - 'Blue'	(77,600) '22MERA...'	2.50 ☐
MS26	*MS26*	£2	8/90	COLOURFUL WAY TO CALL - 'Purple'	(77,049) '22MERB...'	2.50 ☐
MS27	*MS27*	£2	8/90	COLOURFUL WAY TO CALL - 'Yellow'	(75,007) '22MERC...'	2.50 ☐
MS28	*MS28*	£4	8/90	COLOURFUL WAY TO CALL - 'Green'	(74,556) '22MERD...'	4.50 ☐
MS28(a)					'2MERD...'	4.50 ☐
MS28(b)					'25MERA...'	4.50 ☐
MS29	*MS29*	£4	8/90	COLOURFUL WAY TO CALL - 'Pink'	(76,216) '22MERE...'	4.50 ☐
MS30	*(MS28)*	£4	12/90	COLOURFUL WAY TO CALL - 'Green'	(172,000) '20MERD...'/W *C*	4.50 ☐
MS31	*MS31*	£2	12/90	COLOURFUL CHRISTMAS 90 - 'Blue'	(9925) '20MERC...'	2.50 ☐
MS31(a)					(incl. above) '20MERC...'/W	2.50 ☐
MS31(b)					(incl. above) '20MERC...'/W *C*	2.50 ☐
MS32	*MS32*	£2	12/90	COLOURFUL CHRISTMAS 90 - 'Yellow'	(9874) '20MERC...'	2.50 ☐
MS33	*MS33*	£4	12/90	COLOURFUL CHRISTMAS 90 - 'Green'	(10,114) '20MERD...'/W	4.50 ☐
MS33(a)					(incl. above) '20MERD...'/W *C*	4.50 ☐

Note 1. MS30 is a quite different card from MS28. It is lighter in its colours, differs is several details of design and has the silver band right across the card with a shorter 'MERCURYCARD' and a larger '4' as in MS32 these cards were for the British troops in the Gulf.

Note 2. MS31 controls ('20MERC...'/W) on white backgrounds are found in two sizes.

MP - PRIVATE CARDS

No.	Ill.	Units	Date	Description		Value
MP1	*MP1*	£2	6/89	NETWORKS 89, Black, blue / white	(775) '15MER...'	75.00 ☐
MP2	*MP2*	£2	9/89	SPIRIT OF ADVENTURE, Multicoloured	(500) '15MER...'	250.00 ☐
MP3	*MP3*	£2	9/89	SIR ERIC SHARP, Multicoloured	(1500) '15MER...'	75.00 ☐
MP4	*MP4*	£2	9/89	INN ON THE PARK, Silver, etc./cream, Large notch, '16MERB..'		25.00 ☐
MP5	*(MP4)*	£2	9/89	INN ON THE PARK, ... (500) Small notch, '15 MER...'		100.00 ☐
MP5(a)		£2	1/90	Small notch, Control '17 MERE...'		3.00 ☐
MP5A	*(MP4)*	£2	9/89	INN ON THE PARK, Tel. 071.., Small notch, '20MERC...'		5.00 ☐
MP5A(a)		£2	9/89	INN ON THE PARK, Tel. 071.., Small notch, '20MERC...'/W		5.00 ☐
MP6	*(MP4)*	£10	2/90	INN ON THE PARK, Gold, etc /cream, Small notch '18MERF...'		15.00 ☐
MP6A	*(MP4)*	£10	2/90	INN ON THE PARK, Tel. 071.., Small notch '20MERE...'/W		12.00 ☐
MP7	*(MP8)*	£2	10/89	ORIENT EXPRESS, Multicol., Large notch (1000) '16MERB...'		100.00 ☐
MP8	*MP8*	£2	10/89	ORIENT EXPRESS, Multicol., Small notch (1050) '17MERE...'		35.00 ☐

Note. MP7 and MP8 also differ somewhat in their colouring.

No.	Ill.	Units	Date	Description		Value
MP9	*(MP10)*	£0.50	10/89	ABRAXAS. Multicolour. Large notch	(600) '18MERD...'	80.00 ☐
MP10	*MP10*	£0.50	10/89	ABRAXAS. Multicolour. Small notch	(1300) '18MERD...'	20.00 ☐
MP10(a)			4/90	Small notch, Tel. 071 387 5599	(1500) '18MERD...'	10.00 ☐
MP11	*MP11*	£2	10/89	DOCKLANDS TELECOMS CENTRE, Multicolour.	(1525) '18MERC...'	30.00 ☐
MP12	*MS12*	£1	11/89	IT DIRECTION, Red, grey, etc. / white	(2003) '18MERC...'	25.00 ☐
MP13	*MP13*	£2	11/89	HARBOUR SCENE, UK-FRANCE CABLE	(1589) '17MERE...'	25.00 ☐
MP13(a)					(incl. above) '18MERA...'	50.00 ☐
MP14	*MP14*	£2	11/89	VESSELS CLOSE HAULED, UK-NETHER. CABLE.	(1428) '17MERE...'	25.00 ☐
MP15	*MP15*	£2	11/89	GREAT EASTERN, Multicoloured	(1964) '17MERE...'	25.00 ☐

MS12

MS13

MS14

MS15

MS16

MS17

MS18

MS19

MS20

MS21

MS22

MS25

MS26

MS27

MS28

MS29

MS31

MS32

MS33

MP - PRIVATE CARDS

MP1

MP2

MP3

MP4

MP8

MP10

MP11

MP12

MP13

MP14

MP15

MP16

MP17

MP18

MP19

MP21

MP23

MP24

MP25

MP27

MP29

No.	Ill.	Units	Date	Description	Value
MP16	*MP16*	£2	1/90	HARRODS, Multicoloured, Small notch, '18MERA...'	3.00 □
MP16(a)				'20MERC...'	3.00 □
MP16(b)				'15MER...' (500?)	50.00 □
MP16A	*(MP16)*	£2	1/90	HARRODS, Multicoloured, Large notch, '16MERB...'	50.00 □
MP16A(a)				Large notch, '14MER...'	75.00 □
MP17	*MP17*	£2	1/90	SWALLOW HOTELS, Multicoloured, Tel. 01.., '18MERA...'	15.00 □
MP17A	*(MP17)*	£2		SWALLOW HOTELS, Multicoloured, Tel 071.., '19MERC...'	3.00 □
MP17A(a)				Tel 071.., '20MERC...'/W	3.00 □
MP18	*MP18*	£10	1/90	SWALLOW HOTELS, Multicoloured, Large notch '18MERF...'	40.00 □
MP18(a)				Small notch '18MERF...'	40.00 □
MP18A	(MP18)	£10	?/90	SWALLOW HOTELS, Multicoloured, Tel. 071.., '19MERF...'	12.00 □
MP19	*MP19*	£1	2/90	BROADGATE, Multicoloured (6000) '20MERB...'	10.00 □
MP19(a)				(incl. above) '18MERC...'	10.00 □
MP19A				BROADGATE, Multicoloured, Deep notch	300.00 □
MP20	--	£0.50	2/90	NatWest, Multicoloured (1000) (Ill. forbidden) '18MERD...'	60.00 □
MP21	*MP21*	£2	3/90	ManuLife, Multicol. (1300) Tel. No. 01 256 5858 '18MERA...'	7.50 □
MP21(a)				(incl. above) '20MERC...'	3.00 □
MP22	*(MP21)*	£2	3/90	ManuLife, Multicol. (1700) Tel. No. 0276 51888 '18MERA...'	7.50 □
MP22(a)				(incl. above) '20MERC...'	3.00 □
MP23	*MP23*	£0.50	3/90	STANLEY GIBBONS - 150 YEARS, Black/Gold (6000) '18MERD...'	3.00 □
MP23A		£0.50	3/90	STANLEY GIBBONS - 150 YEARS, Black/Gold, Deep notch	75.00 □
MP24	*MP24*	£0.50	3/90	SPACE MANAGEMENT SERVICES, Multicoloured (2216) '18MERD...'	10.00 □
MP25	*MP25*	£0.50	3/90	PARAGON COMMUNICATIONS, Black,blue/white (3000) '18MERD...'	10.00 □
MP25(a)				Error: Logo missing at top left.	--- □
MP26	*(MP27)*	£0.50	3/90	BRIAN REEVES, Black/gold, Tel. 01-2391 (3500) '18MERD...'	5.00 □
MP27	*MP27*	£0.50	3/90	BRIAN REEVES, Black/gold, Tel. 071-2391 (4500) '18MERD...'	3.00 □
MP28	*(MP27)*	£0.50	3/90	BRIAN REEVES, Black/gold, Tel. 071-3780 (4500) '18MERD...'	3.00 □
MP29	*MP29*	£2	4/90	BATTLE OF BRITAIN EXP. Multicoloured (3140) '20MERC...'	3.50 □
MP29(a)				(incl. above) '1MDCC...'	3.50 □
MP29(b)				(incl. above)'17MERE...'	3.50 □
MP29(c)				(incl. above)'18MERA...'	3.50 □
MP30	*MP30*	£2	4/90	B OF B EXP.- SPITFIRE, Multicol. (12,758)'20MERC...'	3.50 □
MP30(a)				(incl. above)'20MERC...'/W	350.00 □
MP30(b)				(incl. above) '1MDCC...'	7.00 □
MP31	*MP31*	£2	4/90	B OF B EXP.- DOGFIGHT, Multicol. (12,306)'20MERC...'	3.50 □
MP31(a)				(incl. above)'20MERC...'/W	3.50 □
MP32	*MP32*	£2	4/90	B OF B EXP.- HURRICANE, Multicol. (12,902)'20MERC...'	3.50 □
MP32(a)				(incl. above)'20MERC...'/W	3.50 □
MP32(b)				(incl. above)'19MERC...'	3.50 □
MP33	*MP33*	£0.50	4/90	BMP BUSINESS, Black, red, white etc (2360) '18MERD...'	10.00 □
MP34	*MP34*	£0.50	4/90	COOPER-BMW, Multicoloured (7399) '19MERA...'	5.00 □
MP34(a)				(incl. above) '18MERD...'	8.00 □
MP35	*MP35*	£2	4/90	MADAM TUSSAUDS, Multicoloured (4504) '19MERC...'	5.00 □
MP35(a)				(incl. above) '20MERC...'	4.00 □
MP36	*MP36*	£0.50	5/90	MOTIVATION STRATEGY, Black,blue,white (7503) '19MERA...'	10.00 □
MP36(a)				'18MERD...'	20.00 □
MP36(b)				'20MERA...'/W	10.00 □
MP37	*MP37*	£0.50	5/90	"ALLO ALLO" Tel. 071.., Multicoloured (3514) '19MERA...'	5.00 □
MP37(a)				(incl. above) '18MERD...'	5.00 □
MP38	*(MP37)*	£0.50	10/90	"ALLO ALLO" Tel. 0908., Multicoloured (6065) '20MERC...'/W	3.50 □

General Note. Where no number of cards issued is given, as in the cases of MP4, MP6 and MP 16, 17 and 18 above, it is normally because these are continuing issues which will be reordered as required and it will only be possible to give a total number when the design is discontinued. They are, in effect, 'private definitives'.

No.	Ill.	Units	Date	Description	Value
MP39	*MP39*	£2	5/90	GKN SANKEY, Multicoloured (3400) '1MDCC...'	2.50 ☐
MP40	*MP40*	£1	5/90	TMA, Multicoloured (4203) Small notch, '20MERB...'	3.00 ☐
MP41	*(MP40)*	£1	5/90	TMA, Multicoloured (incl. above) Large notch, '20MERB...'	100.00 ☐
MP42	*MP42*	£0.50	6/90	INTERNATIONAL THOMSON, Multicoloured (3930) '20MERA...'/W	1.50 ☐
MP43	*MP43*	£0.50	6/90	FIRST TEAM, Multicoloured (3528) Small notch '20MERA...'	5.00 ☐
MP43(a)				(incl. above) Small notch '18MERD...'	5.00 ☐
MP43(b)				(incl. above) Small notch '20MERA...'/W	5.00 ☐
MP44	*(MP43)*	£0.50	6/90	FIRST TEAM, Multicoloured Large notch '20MERA...'	100.00 ☐
MP45	*MP45*	£2	6/90	RED LION SQUARE, Multicoloured (3483) '19MERC...'	12.00 ☐
MP45(a)				(incl. above) '1MDCC...'	12.00 ☐
MP45(b)				(incl. above) '20MERC...'	12.00 ☐
MP45(c)				(incl. above) '20MERC...'/W	3.00 ☐
MP46	*MP46*	£2	6/90	FINANCIAL TIMES-TOKYO, Multicoloured (4283) '20MERC...'/W	3.00 ☐
MP47	*MP47*	£2	7/90	FINLAND FOX, Multicoloured (3926) '20MERC...'/W	3.00 ☐
MP48	*MP48*	£0.50	7/90	COTTAGES - HARBOUR, Multicoloured (3972) '20MERA...'/W	5.00 ☐
MP48(a)				Bluer tones, 'U' 2mm from top (800) '20MERA...'/W	25.00 ☐
MP49	*MP49*	£0.50	7/90	COTTAGES - SUMMER, Multicoloured (3100) '20MERA...'/W	5.00 ☐
MP50	*MP50*	£0.50	7/90	COTTAGES - WINTER, Multicoloured (4202) '20MERA...'/W	5.00 ☐
MP50(a)				Browner tones, 'U' 2mm from top (800) '20MERA...'/W	25.00 ☐

Note. 800 copies of MP48 and of MP 50 were reprinted at the request of Character Country Cottages. They are quite markedly different in colour and the surface is more glossy. The writing at the top has been dropped from 1mm to 2mm from the top edge of the card. Please note that these cards are no longer available from Character Country Cottages who should not be approached for them.

No.	Ill.	Units	Date	Description	Value
MP51	*MP51*	£2	7/90	RAC, Grey, yellow (7174) '20MERC...'/W	2.50 ☐
MP52	*MP52*	£5	7/90	RAC, Multicoloured (7213) Small notch '18MERE...'	7.50 ☐
MP52(a)				(incl. above) Small notch '20MERC...'/W	7.50 ☐
MP52(b)				(incl. above) Small notch '20MERC...'	7.50 ☐
MP53	*(MP52)*	£5	7/90	RAC, Multicoloured (incl. above) Large notch '18MERE...'	25.00 ☐
MP54	*MP54*	£10	7/90	RAC, Gold, blue (4430) Small notch '20MERE...'/W	12.00 ☐
MP55	*(MP54)*	£10	7/90	RAC, Gold, blue (incl. above) Large notch '20MERE...'	25.00 ☐
MP56	*MP56*	£1	8/90	TOOTAL LEISURE, Multicoloured (3829) '18MER...'	2.00 ☐
MP56(a)				(incl. above) '20MERC...'	2.00 ☐
MP56(b)				(incl. above) '20MERB...'/W	2.00 ☐
MP56A	*(MP56)*	£1	8/90	TOOTAL LEISURE, Multicol. Deep notch '??MER?...'	-- ☐
MP57	*MP57*	£1	8/90	MERCURY - JAMES BOND, Red, grey, white (5200) '20MERB...'	2.00 ☐
MP58	*MP58*	£0.50	8/90	HENRY VIII, Multicoloured (5804) '20MERA...'/W	1.50 ☐
MP59	*MP59*	£0.50	8/90	GLEN MILLER, Multicoloured (5726) '20MERA...'/W	1.50 ☐
MP60	*MP60*	£0.50	8/90	LA COCHONNET, Black, pink, white (5184) '20MERA...'/W	1.50 ☐
MP61	*MP61*	£2	8/90	SCANDIC HOTEL, Tel 071 84*3*.. Multicol. (500) '20MERC...'/W	35.00 ☐
MP62	*MP62*	£4	8/90	SCANDIC HOTEL, Tel 071 84*3*.. Multicol.(1000) '20MERD...'/W	40.00 ☐
MP62(a)				'18MERB...'	100.00 ☐
MP63	*MP63*	£5	8/90	SCANDIC HOTEL, Tel 071 84*3*.. Multicol.(1000) '20MERF...'/W	35.00 ☐

Note. These cards have the wrong telephone number and were replaced by MP78 - MP80 below.

No.	Ill.	Units	Date	Description	Value
MP64	*MP64*	£2	2/91	PARK LANE HOTEL, Multicoloured () '20MERC...'/W	2.50 ☐
MP65	*MP65*	£5	8/90	PARK LANE HOTEL, Multicoloured (5007) '20MERF...'/W	6.00 ☐
MP66	*MP66*	£10	8/90	PARK LANE HOTEL, Multicoloured (5335) '20MERE...'/W	12.00 ☐
MP66(a)				(incl. above) '18MERF...'	20.00 ☐
MP66A	*(MP66)*	£10	8/90	PARK LANE HOTEL, Deep notch (incl. above) '20MERE...'/W	20.00 ☐
MP67	*MP67*	£0.50	9/90	IDC - GLASS ENGRAVING, Multicoloured (5259) '20MERA...'/W	2.50 ☐
MP67(a)				(incl. above) '18MERD...'	2.50 ☐
MP68	*MP68*	£0.50	9/90	LEAGUE OF NATIONS - UK, Multicol. (5517) '20MERA...'/W	3.00 ☐
MP69	*MP69*	£0.50	9/90	LEAGUE OF NATIONS - USA, Multicol. (4643)'20MERA...'/W	3.00 ☐
MP69(a)				(incl. above)'18MERD...'	3.00 ☐
MP69(b)				(incl. above) '1MDCC...'	6.00 ☐
MP70	*MP70*	£0.50	9/90	LEAGUE OF NATIONS - RUSSIA, Multicol. (4943) '20MERA...'/W	3.00 ☐
MP71	*MP71*	£0.50	9/90	LEAGUE OF NATIONS - FRANCE, Multicol. (5196) '20MERA...'/W	3.00 ☐

MP30

MP31

MP32

MP33

MP34

MP35

MP36

MP37

MP39

MP40

MP42

MP43

MP45

MP46

MP47

MP48

MP49

MP50

MP51

MP52

MP54

MP56

MP57

MP58

MP59

MP60

MP61

MP62

MP63

MP64

MP65

MP66

MP67

MP68

MP69

MP70

No.	Ill.	Units	Date	Description	Value
MP72	*MP72*	£0.50	9/90	JUNGLE - LEOPARD, Multicol. (5569) '20MERA...'/W	3.00 ☐
MP73	*MP73*	£0.50	9/90	JUNGLE - PARROT, Multicol. (5581) '20MERA...'/W	3.00 ☐
MP74	*MP74*	£0.50	9/90	JUNGLE - SNAKE, Multicol. (5571) '18MERD...'	3.00 ☐
MP75	*MP75*	£0.50	9/90	JUNGLE - CHIMPANZEE, Multicol. (4959) '18MERD...'	5.00 ☐
MP76	*MP76*	£0.50	9/90	JUNGLE - ZEBRA, Multicol. (5202) '18MERD...'	3.00 ☐
MP77	*MP77*	£0.50	9/90	JUNGLE - ELEPHANT, Multicol. (5465) '20MERA...'/W	3.00 ☐

Note. The control number on MP72 is found in two different sizes. The six cards fit together to make a single picture - two across by three down in the above order.

No.	Ill.	Units	Date	Description	Value
MP78	*(MP61)*	£2	9/90	SCANDIC HOTEL, Tel 071 834.. Multicol. (6910)'20MERC...'/W	2.50 ☐
MP79	*(MP62)*	£4	9/90	SCANDIC HOTEL, Tel 071 834.. Multicol. (5409)'18MERB...'	10.00 ☐
MP79(a)				(incl. above) '20MERD...'	4.50 ☐
MP80	*(MP63)*	£5	9/90	SCANDIC HOTEL, Tel 071 834.. Multicol. (5728)'20MERF...'/W	6.00 ☐
MP81	*MP81*	£2	9/90	ORIENT EXPRESS-LEEDS CASTLE, Multicol. (5288) '20MERC...'/W	2.50 ☐
MP81(a)				(incl. above)'18MERA...	2.50 ☐
MP82	*(MP81)*	£2	9/90	OR. EX.-LEEDS CAST. No date, Multicol. (5741) '20MERC...'/W	2.50 ☐
MP82(a)				(incl. above)'18MERA...'	2.50 ☐
MP82(b)				(incl. above)'1MDCC...'	2.50 ☐
MP83	*MP83*	£2	9/90	BUTTERFIELD SIGNS, Multicoloured (5147) '20MERC...'/W	2.50 ☐
MP84	*MP84*	£2	9/90	BOURNMOUTH 1990, Multicoloured (5708) '20MERC...'/W	2.50 ☐
MP84(a)				(incl. above)'20MERC...'	20.00 ☐
MP85	*MP85*	£1	9/90	ADAM HQ, Silver, blue, white (4661) '20MERB...'/W	1.50 ☐
MP86	*MP86*	£1	10/90	CPM - BUSTER KEATON, Multicoloured (5133) '20MERB...'/W	1.50 ☐
MP87	*MP87*	£0.50	10/90	CABLE OPERATOR, Multicoloured (4973) '20MERA...'/W	1.00 ☐
MP88	*(MP87)*	£2	10/90	CABLE OPERATOR, Multicoloured (5683) '20MERC...'/W	2.50 ☐
MP89	*MP89*	£2	11/90	ALUPLAN, Multicoloured (5700) '20MERC...'/W	2.50 ☐
MP89(a)				(incl. above)'20MERC...'	2.50 ☐
MP90	*MP90*	£0.50	11/90	ROBERT SWAN, Multicoloured (5318) '20MERA...'/W	1.00 ☐
MP91	*(MP90)*	£2	11/90	ROBERT SWAN, Multicoloured (5416) '20MERC...'/W	2.50 ☐
MP91(a)				(incl. above) '20MERC...'	2.50 ☐
MP92	*MP92*	£1	11/90	"RACING DRIVER", Multicoloured (5605) '20MERC...'/W	1.50 ☐
MP92(a)				(incl. above) '20MERB...'	1.50 ☐
MP93	*MP93*	£1	11/90	MOUNT FUJI, Multicoloured (5269) '20MERB...'/W	1.50 ☐
MP93(a)				(incl. above) '20MERB...'	1.50 ☐
MP94	*MP94*	£5	11/90	51 / 55, Multicoloured (4610) '20MERF...'/W	6.00 ☐
MP95	*MP95*	£2	11/90	PAKNET, Multicoloured (5821) '20MERA...'/W	2.50 ☐
MP95(a)				(incl. above) '20MERC...'	2.50 ☐
MP96	*MP96*	£1	11/90	TODAY NEWSPAPER, Multicol.(in pack) (18,145) '20MERB...'/W	8.00 ☐

Note. The 'TODAY' card and its packaging show marked variations in shades of colour.

No.	Ill.	Units	Date	Description	Value
MP97	*MP97*	£0.50	11/90	TRT/FTC - MARCONI, Multicoloured (5722) '20MERA...'/W	1.00 ☐
MP97(a)				'20MERA...'/W *C*	1.00 ☐
MP98	*MP98*	£0.50	11/90	CABLE & WIRELESS TRAVEL, Multicolour (6344) '20MERA...'/W	1.00 ☐
MP98(a)				(incl. above) '20MERA...'	1.00 ☐
MP99	*MP99*	£1	11/90	TMA 23, Multicoloured (5266) '20MERB...'/W	1.50 ☐
MP100	*MP100*	£0.50	12/90	TURBO TRAIN, Multicoloured (5918) '20MERA...'/W	1.00 ☐
MP100(a)				'20MERA...'/W *C*	1.00 ☐
MP101	*MP101*	£0.50	12/90	TSB - SPEEDLINK, Multicoloured (5000) '20MERA...'/W	1.00 ☐
MP101(a)				(incl. above) '20MERA...'	1.00 ☐

GENERAL NOTE. There has been a change in the encoding procedure as a result of which some cards now have no magnetic bands in the top corners on the reverse but have a 'C' in the top right corner. These cards are indicated by *C* in the listings above and below and appear to form a distinct variety.

No.	Ill.	Units	Date	Description	Value

MP102 **MP102** £4 12/90 SUN NEWSPAPER, Multicoloured (17,993) '20MERD...'/W 8.00 □
MP102(a) (incl. above)'20MERD..'/W **C** 8.00 □

Note. MP102 above and MP106 below were issued for British forces serving in Saudi Arabia and were not generally available in the UK.

MP103 **MP103** £1 12/90 THAMES WATER, Blue, black, white (5408) '20MERB...'/W 1.50 □
MP104 **MP104** £2 12/90 ADLINK, Multicoloured (4876) '20MERC...'/W 2.50 □
MP104(a) (incl. above)'20MERC...'/W **C** 2.50 □
MP105 **MP105** £2 12/90 MERCURY CORPORATE CHRISTMAS, Multicol.(10,026)'20MERC..'/W 3.00 □
MP105(a) (incl. above) '20MERC...'/W **C** 3.00 □

Note. This card fitted into two different Christmas cards, one ordinary and one making the sound of a telephone when opened, sent by Mercury staff to business contacts. The controls on these cards are found in two different sizes.

MP106 **MP106** £4 12/90 ROYAL BRITISH LEGION, Multicol. (29,095) '20MERD...'/W **C** 5.00 □

MP107 **MP107** £0.50 12/90 C&W - THREE ORANGES, Multicoloured (4017) '20MERA...'/W 1.00 □
MP107(a) (incl. above)'20MERA..' 1.00 □
MP108 **(MP107)** £2 12/90 C&W - THREE ORANGES, Multicoloured (3725) '20MERC...'/W 2.50 □
MP108(a) (incl. above)'20MERC..'/W **C** 2.50 □

MP109 **MP109** £4 2/91 SCHLUMBERGER-S.A.F.E. Multicoloured (3179) '20MERD...'/W **C** 5.00 □
MP110 **MP110** £4 2/91 SCHLUMBERGER-ANSWERS, Multicoloured (3218) '20MERD...'/W **C** 5.00 □

MP111 **MP111** £1 2/91 FELDENE (PFIZER). Blue, yellow, white () '20MERB...'/W **C** 1.50 □

MP112 **MP112** £0.50 2/91 LOOT - MERCURY, Multicoloured (5072) '20MERA...'/W 1.00 □
MP113 **(MP112)** £2 2/91 LOOT - MERCURY, Multicoloured (3804) '20MERC...'/W **C** 2.50 □

MP114 **MP114** £2 2/91 ROADCHEF, Multicoloured (23,803) '20MERC...'/W 2.50 □
MP115 **(MP114)** £4 2/91 ROADCHEF, Multicoloured (19,856) '20MERD...'/W **C** 5.00 □
MP116 **(MP114)** £10 2/91 ROADCHEF, Multicoloured (11,392) '20MERE...'/W 12.00 □

MP71

MP72

MP73

MP74

MP75

MP76

MP77

MP81

MP83

MP84

MP85

MP86

MP87

MP89

MP90

MP92

MP93

MP94

MP95

MP96

MP97

MP98

MP99

MP100

MP101

MP102

MP103

MP104

MP105

MP106

MP107

MP109

MP110

MP111

MP112

MP114

MP117

MP118

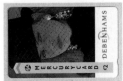

MP119

MP120

MP121

MP122

No.	Ill.	Units	Date	Description				Value	
MP117	*MP117*	£2	2/91	DEBENHAMS - BEDROOM,	Multicol.	(8240)'20MERC...'/W *C*		2.50	☐
MP118	*MP118*	£2	2/91	DEBENHAMS - FAMILY,	Multicol.	(8156)'20MERC...'/W *C*		2.50	☐
MP119	*MP119*	£2	2/91	DEBENHAMS - LADY IN HAT,	Multicol.	(8308)'20MERC...'/W *C*		2.50	☐
MP120	*MP120*	£2	2/91	DEBENHAMS - MAN,	Multicol.	(7756)'20MERC...'/W *C*		2.50	☐
MP121	*MP121*	£2	2/91	DEBENHAMS - DOG AND GIRL,	Multicol.	(8123)'20MERC...'/W *C*		2.50	☐
MP122	*MP122*	£2	2/91	DEBENHAMS - GIRL AND BOY,	Multicol.	(8000)'20MERC...'/W *C*		2.50	☐
MP123	*MP123*	£10	2/91	GULF CARD - M.O.D.- FLAGS,		(50,100) '20MERE...'/W *C*		12.50	☐
MP124	*MP124*	£10	3/91	GULF CARD - BRITISH AEROSPACE,		(15,000) '20MERE...'/W *C*		12.50	☐
MP125	*(MP124)*	£10	3/91	GULF CARD - CABLE & WIRELESS,		(15,000) '20MER?...'/W *C*		12.50	☐
MP126	*(MP124)*	£10	3/91	GULF CARD - NATIONAL WESTMINSTER,	(15,000) '20MERE...'/W *C*			12.50	☐
MP127	*MP127*	£2	2/91	CABLE & WIRELESS-EUROPE, Tel.'666' (5252) '20MERC...'/W *C*				2.50	☐
MP127(a)				Error. Frankfurt Tel. No. '600' (30) '20MERC...'/W *C*				----	☐

Note. 127(a) was agreed by and sent to the sponsors before the error was noted and all but 30 cards which had already been issued in Germany were immediately withdrawn.

MP128	*MP128*	£2	3/91	CUPRINOL, Multicoloured (6902) '20MERC...'/W *C*	2.50	☐
MP129	*MP129*	£2	3/91	LIVERPOOL AIRPORT, Multicoloured (5000) '20MERC...'/W *C*	2.50	☐
MP130	*MP130*	£2	4/91	HANBURY MANOR, Multicoloured (???) '20MERC...'/W *C*	2.50	☐
MP131	----	£5	4/91	HANBURY MANOR, Multicoloured (???) '20MER?...'/W *C*	2.50	☐
MP132	*MP132*	£10	4/91	HANBURY MANOR, Multicoloured (???) '20MER?...'/W *C*	2.50	☐
MP133	*MP133*	£0.50	4/91	HAAGAN DAZS, Multicoloured (4500) '20MERA...'/W *C*	2.50	☐
MP134	*MP134*	£1	4/91	STANSTED AIRPORT, Multicoloured (45,000) '20MERB...'/W *C*	2.50	☐
MP135	*MP135*	£0.50	4/91	HARRY ENFIELD, Black, blue (???) '20MERA...'	1.00	☐
MP135(a)				(incl. above) '20MERA...'/W	1.00	☐
MP136	*MP136*	£2	4/91	HARRY ENFIELD - SIMPLE, Black, blue (???) '20MER?...'/W	2.50	☐
MP137	*MP137*	£2	4/91	HARRY ENFIELD - INSERT, Black, blue (???) '20MERD...'/W *C*	2.50	☐
MP138	*(MP135)*	£4	4/91	HARRY ENFIELD - PUSH, Black, blue (???) '20MER?...'/W	5.00	☐
MP139	*(MP140)*	£0.50	4/91	THE PRINCE'S TRUST. Multicoloured (8000) '20MER?...'/W *C*	1.00	☐
MP140	*MP140*	£2	4/91	THE PRINCE'S TRUST. Multicoloured (5000) '20MERC...'/W *C*	1.00	☐
MP141	----	£0.50	4/91	CONCEPT SERVICES, Multicoloured () '20MER?...'/ *C*	1.00	☐
MP142	*MP142*	£2	4/91	BELL BUILDING, Multicoloured () '20MER?...'/W *C*	2.50	☐
MP143	----	£0.50	4/91	DUTCH TOURIST BOARD, Multicoloured () '20MER?...'/W *C*	1.00	☐
MP144	----	£0.50	4/91	TOP UK INSURANCE, Multicoloured () '20MER?...'/W *C*	1.00	☐
MP145	*MP145*	£1	4/91	SANKEY VENDING, Multicoloured () '20MER?...'/W *C*	1.50	☐
MP146	----	£1	4/91	WOLSEY PARK, Multicoloured () '20MER?...'/W *C*	1.50	☐

INTERNAL CARD

MI1	*MI1*	£2	12/89	MOBILE SERVICES-CHRISTMAS PARTY (114) '8MERA...'	---	☐

Note. MI1 was an internal invitation card. None is known to have come onto the market yet and, as with all such cards, no realistic price can be given at this stage.

MT - TEST CARDS

MT1	*MT1*	1000	1986?	Red, blue, white	75.00	☐
MT2	*(MT1)*	1000	1990?	Red, blue, white, Control on silver	75.00	☐
MT3	*MT3*	--	1991?	MERCURY ENGINEERS / TEST CARD. Black on white.	--	☐

Note 1. MT1, although the standard test cards for GPT systems, also formed the basis of the China (Shanghai) and Canadian trial cards and for the Irish 'Cork card'.

Note 2. The wording on MT3 is on two lines in 3mm thin italic capitals towards the top right of the card.

MERCURY NUMBERS

When Mercury and Paytelco cards are issued they are assigned numbers by Mercury and they are often listed for sale under these numbers. The Mercury numbers are not suitable for a specialised listing such as in this book since they are purely consecutive and make no distinction between different classes of cards such as Definitive and Private cards. Collectors might, however, find a cross-reference list useful and this is given below with Mercury consecutive numbers (MER...) and Paytelco numbers (PAY... etc.) on the left and the corresponding catalogue (and therefore illustration) numbers against them on the right.

MER 0001	MS1	MER 0061	MP17A	MER 0121	MP89	MER 0181	MP146	PAY 0041	PTT5
MER 0002	MS2	MER 0062	MP18A	MER 0122	MP90	MER 0182	MP133	PAY 0042	PTS12
MER 0003	MS3	MER 0063	MP5A&a	MER 0123	MP91	MER 0183	MP135	PAY 0043	
MER 0004	MD1	MER 0064	MP37	MER 0124	MP92	MER 0184	MP136	PAY 0044	
MER 0005	MD2	MER 0065	MP39	MER 0125	MP6A	MER 0185	MP137	PAY 0045	
MER 0006	MD3	MER 0066	MP40/1	MER 0126	MS31	MER 0186	MP138	PAY 0046	PTS13
MER 0007	MC1	MER 0067	MP42	MER 0127	MS32	MER 0187	MP140	PAY 0047	PTS14
MER 0008	MS5	MER 0068	MP43/4	MER 0128	MS33	MER 0188		PAY 0048	PTS15
MER 0009	MS6	MER 0069	MP45	MER 0129	MP93	MER 0189		PAY 0049	
MER 0010	MS7	MER 0070	MP46	MER 0130	MP94	MER 0190		PAY 0050	
MER 0011	MS4	MER 0071	MP47	MER 0131	MP95	MER 0191		PAY 0051	
MER 0012	MS8	MER 0072	MP56/A	MER 0132	MP96	MER 0192		PAY 0052	
MER 0013	MS9	MER 0073	MP48	MER 0133	MP97	MER 0193			
MER 0014	MS10	MER 0074	MP49	MER 0134	MP98	MER 0194			
MER 0015	MC2	MER 0075	MP50	MER 0135	MP99	MER 0195	MP139		
MER 0016	MS11	MER 0076	MP57	MER 0136	MP100	MER 0196		PFA 0001	PTF1
MER 0017	MS12	MER 0077	MC3	MER 0137	MP101	MER 0197		PFA 0002	PTF3
MER 0018	MS14	MER 0078	MP51	MER 0138	MP102	MER 0198		PFA 0003	PTF5
MER 0019	MS15	MER 0079	MP52/3	MER 0139	MP103	MER 0199		PFA 0004	PTF7
MER 0020	MS13	MER 0080	MP54/5	MER 0140	MP104			PFA 0005	PTF9
MER 0021	MP1	MER 0081	MP58	MER 0141	MP105	PAY 0001	PTB2&8	PFA 0006	PTF11
MER 0022	MP2	MER 0082	MP59	MER 0142	MP106	PAY 0002	PTB3&9	PFA 0007	PTF13
MER 0023	MP3	MER 0083	MP61	MER 0143	MP108	PAY 0003	PTB1&7	PFA 0008	PTF15
MER 0024	MP4	MER 0084	MP62	MER 0144	MS30	PAY 0004	PTB4&10	PFA 0009	PTF17
MER 0025	MP9&10	MER 0085	MP63	MER 0145	MP109	PAY 0005	PTB5&11	PFA 0010	PTF19
MER 0026	MS16	MER 0086	MP60	MER 0146	MP107	PAY 0006	PTB6&12	PFA 0011	PTF21
MER 0027	MS17	MER 0087	MP65	MER 0147	MP111	PAY 0007	PTO1	PFA 0012	PTF23
MER 0028	MS18	MER 0088	MP66	MER 0148	MP129	PAY 0008	PTO2	PFA 0013	PTF25
MER 0029	MS19	MER 0089	MP64	MER 0149		PAY 0009	PTO3	PFA 0014	PTF27
MER 0030	MS20	MER 0090	MS23	MER 0150	MP114	PAY 0010	PTS1	PFA 0015	PTF29
MER 0031	MP7&8	MER 0091	MP67	MER 0151	MP115	PAY 0011	PTS5	PFA 0016	
MER 0032	MP14	MER 0092	MP68	MER 0152	MP116	PAY 0012	PTS2	PFA 0017	
MER 0033	MP11	MER 0093	MP69	MER 0153		PAY 0013	PTS3	PFA 0018	
MER 0034	MP12	MER 0094	MP70	MER 0154	MP117	PAY 0014	PTS6	PFA 0019	
MER 0035	MP15	MER 0095	MP71	MER 0155	MP118	PAY 0015	PTS4	PFA 0020	
MER 0036	MP13	MER 0096	MP74	MER 0156	MP119	PAY 0016	PTS7	PFA 0021	PTF2
MER 0037	MS21	MER 0097	MP75	MER 0157	MP120	PAY 0017	PTT1	PFA 0022	PTF4
MER 0038	MP17	MER 0098	MP72	MER 0158	MP122	PAY 0018	PTT2	PFA 0023	PTF6
MER 0039	MP18	MER 0099	MP73	MER 0159	MP121	PAY 0019	PTP2	PFA 0024	PTF14
MER 0040	MP16	MER 0100	MP77	MER 0160	MP112	PAY 0020	PTP3	PFA 0025	PTF10
MER 0041	MP6	MER 0101	MP76	MER 0161	MP113	PAY 0021	PTP4	PFA 0026	PTF8
MER 0042	MP19	MER 0102	MS25	MER 0162		PAY 0022	PTP5	PFA 0027	PTF16
MER 0043	MP20	MER 0103	MS27	MER 0163	MP134	PAY 0023	PTP1	PFA 0028	PTF18
MER 0044	MP21	MER 0104	MS26	MER 0164	MP123	PAY 0024	PTP6	PFA 0029	PTF20
MER 0045	MP22	MER 0105	MS28	MER 0165	MP110	PAY 0025	PTM1	PFA 0030	PTF22
MER 0046	MP23	MER 0106	MS29	MER 0166	MP127	PAY 0026	PTS9	PFA 0031	PTF24
MER 0047	MP25	MER 0107	MP78	MER 0167	MP125	PAY 0027	PTS11	PFA 0032	PTF26
MER 0048	MP24	MER 0108	MP79	MER 0168	MP124	PAY 0028	PTS10	PFA 0033	PTF28
MER 0049	MP26	MER 0109	MP80	MER 0169	MP126	PAY 0029	PTS8	PFA 0034	PTF30
MER 0050	MP27	MER 0110	MS24	MER 0170		PAY 0030		PFA 0035	PTF32
MER 0051	MP28	MER 0111	MP81	MER 0171	MP142	PAY 0031	PTA1	PFA 0036	PTF34
MER 0052	MP10A	MER 0112	MP82	MER 0172	MP106?	PAY 0032	PTA3	PFA 0037	
MER 0053	MP29	MER 0113	MP83	MER 0173	MP144	PAY 0033	PTA4	PFA 0038	
MER 0054	MP30	MER 0114	MP38	MER 0174		PAY 0034	PTA5	PFA 0039	
MER 0055	MP31	MER 0115	MP84	MER 0175	MP128	PAY 0035	PTP7	PFA 0040	
MER 0056	MP32	MER 0116	MP86	MER 0176		PAY 0036	PTP8	PFA 0041	
MER 0057	MP33	MER 0117	MS22	MER 0177	MP130	PAY 0037	PTP9	PFA 0042	
MER 0058	MP34	MER 0118	MP85	MER 0178	MP131	PAY 0038	PTP10	PFA 0043	
MER 0059	MP35	MER 0119	MP87	MER 0179	MP132	PAY 0039	PTT3	PFA 0044	
MER 0060	MP36	MER 0120	MP88	MER 0180	MP145	PAY 0040	PTT4	PFA 0045	

MP123

MP124

MP127

MP128

MP129

MP130

MP132

MP133

MP134

MP135

MP136

MP137

MP140

MP142

MP145

MI1

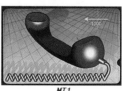

MT1

MT3

Call.Collect.

The Irish Collection from Telecom Ireland

Now Telecom Ireland offers you the opportunity to join one of the fastest growing collectors clubs in Europe. Irish CallCards are unique and already highly valued. For your free brochure, contact us on Freefone 353 1 1800 441441 or write to Telecom Ireland CallCard Collectors Club, Room 414, Telephone House, Marlborough Street, Dublin 1, Ireland.

CallCard Collection.

37

MT - PAYTELCO MERCURY CARDS

SHELL First Series

No.	Ill.	Units	Date	Description	Value
PTS1	*PTS1*	£0.50	1/90	COMPLIMENTARY. Multicoloured (8724) '1PSHA...'	100.00 □
PTS1(a)				(incl. above) '6PSHA...'	1.00 □
PTS2	*PTS2*	£2	1/90	UNLEADED, Multicoloured (21,399) '1PSHB...'	5.00 □
PTS2(a)				(incl. above) '6PSHB...'	2.50 □
PTS3	*(PTS1)*	£4	1/90	UNLEADED, Multicoloured (8957) '1PSHC...'	8.00 □
PTS3(a)				(incl. above) '6PSHC...'	5.00 □
PTS4	*PTS4*	£10	1/90	UNLEADED, Multicoloured (6046) '1PSHD...'	25.00 □
PTS4(a)				(incl. above) '6PSHD...'	12.00 □

SHELL Second Series

PTS5	*PTS5*	£2	3/90	RACING AHEAD, Multicoloured (155,892) '2PSHA...'(large)	10.00 □
PTS5(a)				(incl. above) '2PSHA...'(small)	2.50 □
PTS6	*PTS6*	£4	3/90	RACING AHEAD, Multicoloured (44,638) '2PSHB...'	15.00 □
PTS6(a)				(incl. above) '5PSHB...'	5.00 □
PTS7	*PTS7*	£10	3/90	RACING AHEAD, Multicoloured (14,428) '2PSHC...'	50.00 □
PTS7(a)				(incl. above) '5PSHC...'	12.00 □

SHELL Third Series - Bar Code added on reverse (except for PTS8).

PTS8	*PTS8*	£0.20	1/90	RIO COMPLIMENTARY. Multicoloured '4PSHA...' (43,860)	1.00 □
PTS9	*(PTS5)*	£2	3/90	RACING AHEAD, Multicoloured (172,193) '3PSHA...'	2.50 □
PTS10	*(PTS6)*	£4	3/90	RACING AHEAD, Multicoloured (45,260) '3PSHB...'	5.00 □
PTS11	*(PTS7)*	£10	3/90	RACING AHEAD, Multicoloured (15,205) '3PSHC...'	12.00 □

SHELL Fourth Series - Bar Code added on reverse (except for PTS12).

PTS12	*(PTS4)*	£0.50	1/90	TREES - COMPLIMENTARY. Multicolour. (3764) '9PSHA...'	1.00 □
PTS13	*(PTS2)*	£2	3/90	UNLEADED (BAR CODE on r.), Multicol. (79,100) '7PSHA...'	2.50 □
PTS14	*(PTS1)*	£4	3/90	UNLEADED (BAR CODE on r.), Multicol. (24,100) '7PSHB...'	5.00 □
PTS15	*(PTS4)*	£10	3/90	UNLEADED (BAR CODE on r.), Multicol. (9050) '7PSHC...'	11.00 □

BOOTS First Series - Black Backs.

PTB1	*PTB1*	£2	3/90	MAKING FACES, Multicoloured (?000) '1PBOB...'	4.00 □
PTB2	*PTB2*	£2	3/90	LUNCHTIME FOODS, Multicoloured (?000) '1PBOD...'	4.00 □
PTB3	*PTB3*	£2	3/90	NAPPY SERVICE, Multicoloured (?000) '1PBOC...'	4.00 □
PTB4	*PTB4*	£2	3/90	FILM PROCESSING, Multicoloured (?000) '1PBOA...'	4.00 □
PTB5	*PTB5*	£4	3/90	No.7, Multicoloured (?000) '1PBOE...'	6.00 □
PTB6	*PTB6*	£10	3/90	OPTICIANS, Multicoloured (?000) '1PBOF...'	15.00 □

BOOTS Second Series - Controls on white background.

PTB7	*(PTB1)*	£2	7/90	MAKING FACES, Multicoloured (46,400) '2PBOB...'/W	3.00 □
PTB8	*(PTB2)*	£2	7/90	LUNCHTIME FOODS, Multicoloured (47,215) '2PBOD...'/W	3.00 □
PTB9	*(PTB3)*	£2	7/90	NAPPY SERVICE, Multicoloured (47,187) '2PBOC...'/W	3.00 □
PTB10	*(PTB4)*	£2	7/90	FILM PROCESSING, Multicoloured (45,036) '2PBOA...'/W	3.00 □
PTB11	*(PTB5)*	£4	7/90	No.7, Multicoloured (48,277) '2PBOE...'/W	5.00 □
PTB12	*(PTB6)*	£10	7/90	OPTICIANS, Multicoloured (13,350) '2PBOF...'/W	12.00 □

TRUSTHOUSE FORTE

PTT1	*PTT1*	£2	3/90	TRAVELODGE I, Multicoloured (32,410) '1PTHA...'	5.00 □
PTT1(a)				(incl. above) '2PTHA...'/W	3.00 □
PTT2	*PTT2*	£2	?/90	TRAVELODGE II, Multicoloured (393,969) '2PTHA...'	5.00 □
PTT2(a)				(incl. above) '3PTHA...'/W	3.00 □
PTT3	*PTT3*	£2	4/91	THF-WELCOME BREAK, Multicoloured (?000) '5PTHA...'/W *C*	2.50 □
PTT4	*PTT4*	£4	4/91	THF-WELCOME BREAK, Multicoloured (?000) '5PTHB...'/W *C*	4.50 □
PTT5	*PTT5*	£10	4/91	THF-WELCOME BREAK, Multicoloured (?000) '5PTHC...'/W *C*	10.50 □

TENET MARKETING

PTM1	*PTM1*	£0.50	3/90	TENET GROUP, Multicoloured (4500) '1PTEA...'	2.50 □

POST OFFICE

No.	Ill.	Units	Date	Description	Value
PTO1	*PTO1*	£2	3/90	COLIN JACKSON, Multicoloured (172,572) '1PPOA...'	5.00 ☐
PTO1(a)				(incl. above)'2PPOA...'/W	2.50 ☐
PTO1(b)				(incl. above)'3PPOA...'	2.50 ☐
PTO2	*PTO2*	£4	3/90	ANDY ASHURST, Multicoloured (84,769) '1PPOB...'	6.00 ☐
PTO2(a)				(incl. above)'2PPOB...'	5.00 ☐
PTO2(b)				(incl. above)'2PPOB...'/W	5.00 ☐
PTO2(c)				(incl. above)'3PPOB...'	5.00 ☐
PTO3	*PTO3*	£10	3/90	DALTON GRANT, Multicoloured (50,638) '1PPOC...'	14.00 ☐
PTO3(a)				(incl. above)'2PPOC...'	12.50 ☐
PTO3(b)				(incl. above)'2PPOC...'/W	12.50 ☐
PTO3(c)				(incl. above)'3PPOC...'	12.50 ☐
PTO4	*PTO4*	£2	3/91	BERYL COOKE, Multicoloured (?000) '4PPOA...'/S	2.50 ☐
PTO5	*PTO5*	£4	3/91	BERYL COOKE, Multicoloured (?000) '4PPOB...'/S	5.00 ☐
PTO6	*PTO6*	£10	3/91	BERYL COOKE, Multicoloured (?000) '4PPOC...'/S	12.50 ☐

Note. Wording on the reverses are in silver and controls are black on silver, shown as /S.

PAYTELCO CARDS

First Series - Animals

PTP1	*PTP1*	£0.50	3/90	COMPLIMENTARY - PARROT, Multicol. (11,100) '1PAYA...'/S	2.00 ☐
PTP2	*PTP2*	£2	3/90	ELEPHANTS, Multicoloured (30,144) '1PAYB...'/S	2.50 ☐
PTP3	*PTP3*	£2	3/90	HIPPOS, Multicoloured (31,226) '1PAYC...'/S	2.50 ☐
PTP4	*PTP4*	£2	3/90	CAMELS, Multicoloured (30,901) '1PAYD...'/S	2.50 ☐
PTP5	*PTP5*	£4	3/90	TIGERS, Multicoloured (11,533) '1PAYE...'/S	5.00 ☐
PTP6	*PTP6*	£10	3/90	PARROTS, Multicoloured (5561) '1PAYF...'/S	12.00 ☐

Second Series - Pop Stars

PTP7	*PTP7*	£2	3/90	KYLIE MINOGUE, Multicoloured (25,513) '1PPSA...'/S	2.50 ☐
PTP8	*PTP8*	£2	3/90	JON BON JOVI, Multicoloured (21,784) '1PPSB...'/S	2.50 ☐
PTP9	*PTP9*	£4	3/90	STONE ROSES, Multicoloured (13,689) '1PPSC...'/S	5.00 ☐
PTP10	*PTP10*	£10	3/90	MADONNA, Multicoloured (10,919) '1PPSD...'/S	12.00 ☐

TERRITORIAL ARMY

PTA1	*PTA1*	£0.50	3/90	TA - SOLDIERS, Multicoloured (23,247) '1PTAA...'/S	1.00 ☐
PTA2	*PTA2*	£2	3/90	TA - ROYAL MARINES, Multicoloured (?000) '1PTAB...'/S	2.50 ☐
PTA3	*PTA3*	£2	3/90	TA - ROYAL NAVY, Multicoloured (?000) '1PTAC...'/S	2.50 ☐
PTA4	*PTA4*	£2	3/90	TA - TECHNICIAN, Multicoloured (?000) '1PTAD...'/S	2.50 ☐
PTA5	*(PTA1)*	£2	3/90	TA - SOLDIERS, Multicoloured (?000) '1PTAE...'/S	2.50 ☐

FOOTBALL LEAGUE

Cards will be issued for most or all of the Football League and the Scottish clubs over the next year or so. These will be sold through Supporters' Clubs for use in telephones in the grounds and will also be available through other outlets. The £2 team photograph card will be changed each year while the £5 club badge card will be permanent (unless the telephone number of the club on the reverse is changed).

PTS1

PTS2

PTS4

PTS5

PTS6

PTS7

PTS8

PTB1

PTB2

PTB3

PTB4

PTB5

PTB6

PTT1

PTT2

PTT3

PTT4

PTT5

PTM1

PTO1

PTO2

PTO3

PTO4

PTO5

PTO6

PTP1

PTP2

PTP3

PTP4

PTP5

PTP6

PTP7

PTP8

PTP9

PTP10

PTA1

PTA2

PTA3

PTA4

PTF1

PTF2

PTF3

No.	Ill.	Units	Date	Description	Value
PTF1	*PTF1*	£2	17/12/90	TOTTENHAM, Multicoloured (11,000) '1PFLA...'/S	2.50 □
PTF2	*PTF2*	£5	14/1/91	TOTTENHAM, Black and white (6000) '?PFLA...'/S	5.50 □
PTF3	*PTF3*	£2	17/12/90	NORWICH CITY, Multicoloured (11,000) '?PFL?...'/S	2.50 □
PTF4	*PTF4*	£5	14/1/91	NORWICH CITY, Yellow, green, black (6000) '?PFL?...'/S	5.50 □
PTF5	*PTF5*	£2	17/12/90	NOTTS FOREST, Multicoloured (11,000) '2PFLB...'/S	2.50 □
PTF6	*PTF6*	£5	14/1/91	NOTTS FOREST, Red and white (6000) '3PFLQ...'/S	5.50 □
PTF7	*PTF7*	£2	17/12/90	Q.P.R., Multicoloured (11,000) '?PFL?...'/S	2.50 □
PTF8	*PTF8*	£5	14/1/91	Q.P.R., Light blue and white (6000) '?PFL?...'/S	5.50 □
PTF9	*PTF9*	£2	17/12/90	DERBY, Multicoloured (11,000) '2PFLH...'/S	2.50 □
PTF10	*PTF10*	£5	14/1/91	DERBY, Black and white (6000) '3PFLT...'/S	5.50 □
PTF11	*PTF11*	£2	17/12/90	OLDHAM, Multicoloured (11,000) '?PFL?...'/S	2.50 □
PTF12	*PTF12*	£5	2/91	OLDHAM, Red, blue, white (2000) '?PFL?...'/S	5.50 □
PTF13	*PTF13*	£2	17/12/90	NOTTS COUNTY, Multicoloured (11,000) '2PFLR...'/S	2.50 □
PTF14	*PTF14*	£5	14/1/91	NOTTS COUNTY, Black and white (6000) '4PFLA...'/S	5.50 □
PTF15	*PTF15*	£2	17/12/90	WATFORD, Multicoloured (11,000) '?PFL?...'/S	2.50 □
PTF16	*PTF16*	£5	14/1/91	WATFORD, Yellow, black, red (6000) '?PFL?...'/S	5.50 □
PTF17	*PTF17*	£2	17/12/90	ASTON VILLA, Multicoloured (11,000) '?PFL?...'/S	2.50 □
PTF18	*PTF18*	£5	14/1/91	ASTON VILLA, Red, blue, yellow (6000) '?PFL?...'/S	5.50 □
PTF19	*PTF19*	£2	17/12/90	WIMBLEDON, Multicoloured (11,000) '?PFL?...'/S	2.50 □
PTF20	*PTF20*	£5	14/1/91	WIMBLEDON, Multicoloured (6000) '?PFL?...'/S	5.50 □
PTF21	*PTF21*	£2	17/12/90	SHEFFIELD UNITED, Multicoloured (11,000) '?PFL?...'/S	2.50 □
PTF22	*PTF22*	£5	14/1/91	SHEFFIELD UNITED, Red, black, white (6000) '?PFL?...'/S	5.50 □
PTF23	*PTF23*	£2	17/12/90	SHEFFIELD WEDNESDAY, Multicoloured (11,000) '2PFLK...'/S	2.50 □
PTF24	*PTF24*	£5	14/1/91	SHEFFIELD WEDNESDAY, Dark blue, white (6000) '3PFLV...'/S	5.50 □
PTF25	*PTF25*	£2	17/12/90	IPSWICH, Multicoloured (11,000) '2PFLN...'/S	2.50 □
PTF26	*PTF26*	£5	14/1/91	IPSWICH, Blue, yellow, white (6000) '3PFLW...'/S	5.50 □
PTF27	*PTF27*	£2	17/12/90	PORTSMOUTH, Multicoloured (11,000) '2PFLL...'/S	2.50 □
PTF28	*PTF28*	£5	14/1/91	PORTSMOUTH, Blue and white (6000) '?PFL?...'/S	5.50 □
PTF29	*PTF29*	£2	17/12/90	CHARLTON, Multicoloured (11,000) '?PFL?...'/S	2.50 □
PTF30	*PTF30*	£5	14/1/91	CHARLTON, Red, black, white (6000) '?PFL?...'/S	5.50 □
PTF31	*PTF31*	£2	2/91	LIVERPOOL, Multicoloured (2000) '?PFL?...'/S	2.50 □
PTF32	*PTF32*	£5	14/1/91	LIVERPOOL, Red and white (6000) '?PFL?...'/S	5.50 □

PTF4

PTF5

PTF6

PTF7

PTF8

PTF9

PTF10

PTF11

PTF12

PTF13

PTF14

PTF15

PTF16

PTF17

PTF18

PTF19

PTF20

PTF21

PTF22

PTF23

PTF24

PTF25

PTF26

PTF27

PTF28

PTF29

PTF30

PTF31

PTF32

PTF34

PTF35

PTF36

PTF37

PTF38

PTF39

PTF40

PTF41

PTF42

PTF45

PTF46

PTF53

PTF54

No.	Ill.	Units	Date	Description	Value
PTF33	---	£2	2/91	FULHAM, Multicoloured (2000) '?PFL?...'/S	2.50 ☐
PTF34	*PTF34*	£5	14/1 91	FULHAM, Multicoloured (4000) '?PFL?...'/S	5.50 ☐
PTF35	*PTF35*	£2	4/91	CRYSTAL PALACE, Multicoloured (2000) '?PFL?...'/S	2.50 ☐
PTF36	*PTF36*	£5	4/91	CRYSTAL PALACE, Blue, red, white (2000) '?PFL?...'/S	5.50 ☐
PTF37	*PTF37*	£2	2/91	HUDDERSFIELD, Multicoloured (2000) '?PFL?...'/S	2.50 ☐
PTF38	*PTF38*	£5	2/91	HUDDERSFIELD, Multicoloured (1000) '?PFL?...'/S	5.50 ☐
PTF39	*PTF39*	£2	2/91	PORT VALE, Multicoloured (5500) '?PFL?...'/S	2.50 ☐
PTF40	*PTF40*	£5	2/91	PORT VALE, Multicoloured (2000) '?PFL?...'/S	5.50 ☐
PTF41	*PTF41*	£2	2/91	WEST HAM, Multicoloured (5500) '?PFL?...'/S	2.50 ☐
PTF42	*PTF42*	£5	2/91	WEST HAM, Light blue, (2000) '?PFL?...'/S	5.50 ☐
PTF43	---	£2	2/91	SOUTHAMPTON, Multicoloured (5500) '?PFL?...'/S	2.50 ☐
PTF44	---	£5	2/91	SOUTHAMPTON, (2000) '?PFL?...'/S	5.50 ☐
PTF45	*PTF45*	£2	2/91	ARSENAL, Multicoloured (5500) '?PFL?...'/S	2.50 ☐
PTF46	*PTF46*	£5	2/91	ARSENAL, Red and white (2000) '?PFL?...'/S	5.50 ☐
PTF47	---	£2	2/91	LEICESTER CITY, Multicoloured (5500) '?PFL?...'/S	2.50 ☐
PTF48	---	£5	2/91	LEICESTER CITY, (2000) '?PFL?...'/S	5.50 ☐
PTF49	---	£2	2/91	LEEDS UNITED, Multicoloured (5500) '?PFL?...'/S	2.50 ☐
PTF50	---	£5	2/91	LEEDS UNITED, (2000) '?PFL?...'/S	5.50 ☐
PTF51	---	£2	2/91	WEST BROMWICH, Multicoloured (5500) '?PFL?...'/S	2.50 ☐
PTF52	---	£5	2/91	WEST BROMWICH, (2000) '?PFL?...'/S	5.50 ☐
PTF53	*PTF53*	£2	2/91	MANCHESTER UNITED, Multicoloured (5500) '?PFL?...'/S	2.50 ☐
PTF54	*PTF54*	£5	2/91	MANCHESTER UNITED, Red, black, yellow (2000) '?PFL?...'/S	5.50 ☐
PTF55	*PTF55*	£2	2/91	BRENTFORD, Multicoloured (2000) '?PFL?...'/S	2.50 ☐
PTF56	*PTF56*	£5	2/91	BRENTFORD, Red, white, black (1000) '?PFL?...'/S	5.50 ☐
PTF57	*PTF57*	£2	4/91	SUNDERLAND, Multicoloured (2000) '?PFL?...'/S	2.50 ☐
PTF58	*PTF58*	£5	4/91	SUNDERLAND, Red and black (2000) '?PFL?...'/S	5.50 ☐
PTF59	*PTF59*	£2	4/91	EVERTON, Multicoloured (5500) '?PFL?...'/S	2.50 ☐
PTF60	*PTF60*	£5	4/91	EVERTON, Blue and white (2000) '?PFL?...'/S	5.50 ☐
PTF61	---	£2	4/91	SOUTHEND, Multicoloured (5500) '?PFL?...'/S	2.50 ☐
PTF62	---	£5	4/91	SOUTHEND, (2000) '?PFL?...'/S	5.50 ☐

No.	Ill.	Units	Date	Description	Value
PTF63	*PTF63*	£2	4/91	BLACKPOOL, Multicoloured (5500) '?PFL?...'/S	2.50 ☐
PTF64	*PTF64*	£5	4/91	BLACKPOOL, Multicoloured (2000) '?PFL?...'/S	5.50 ☐
PTF65	*PTF65*	£2	4/91	WOLVERHAMPTON, Multicoloured (5500) '?PFL?...'/S	2.50 ☐
PTF66	*PTF66*	£5	4/91	WOLVERHAMPTON, Orange and black (2000) '?PFL?...'/S	5.50 ☐
PTF67	*PTF67*	£2	4/91	CHELSEA, Multicoloured (2000) '?PFL?...'/S	2.50 ☐
PTF68	*PTF68*	£5	4/91	CHELSEA, Blue and white (2000) '?PFL?...'/S	5.50 ☐
PTF69	*PTF69*	£2	4/91	MANCHESTER CITY, Multicoloured (500) '?PFL?...'/S	2.50 ☐
PTF70	*PTF70*	£5	4/91	MANCHESTER CITY, Multicoloured (500) '?PFL?...'/S	5.50 ☐
PTF71	*PTF71*	£2	4/91	MIDDLESBROUGH, Multicoloured (500) '?PFL?...'/S	2.50 ☐
PTF72	*PTF72*	£5	4/91	MIDDLESBROUGH, Red, white, black (500) '?PFL?...'/S	5.50 ☐

SCOTTISH CLUBS

No.	Ill.	Units	Date	Description	Value
PTF100	*PTF100*	£2	4/91	CELTIC, Multicoloured (2000)	2.50 ☐
PTF101	*PTF101*	£5	4/91	CELTIC, Green and white (1500)	5.50 ☐
PTF102	*PTF102*	£2	4/91	MOTHERWELL, Multicoloured (2000)	2.50 ☐
PTF103	*PTF103*	£5	4/91	MOTHERWELL, Orange and purple (1500)	5.50 ☐
PTF104	*PTF104*	£2	4/91	ABERDEEN, Multicoloured (2000)	2.50 ☐
PTF105	*PTF105*	£5	4/91	ABERDEEN, Red and white (1500)	5.50 ☐
PTF106	*PTF106*	£2	4/91	DUNFERMLINE, Multicoloured (2000)	2.50 ☐
PTF107	*PTF107*	£5	4/91	DUNFERMLINE, Black and white (1500)	5.50 ☐
PTF108	*PTF108*	£2	4/91	ST. MIRREN, Multicoloured (2000)	2.50 ☐
PTF109	*PTF109*	£5	4/91	ST. MIRREN, Multicoloured (1500)	5.50 ☐
PTF110	*PTF110*	£2	4/91	DUNDEE, Multicoloured (2000)	2.50 ☐
PTF111	*PTF111*	£5	4/91	DUNDEE, Orange, black, red (1500)	5.50 ☐
PTF112	*PTF112*	£2	4/91	HEARTS, Multicoloured (2000)	2.50 ☐
PTF113	*PTF113*	£5	4/91	HEARTS, Multicoloured (1500)	5.50 ☐
PTF114	*PTF114*	£2	4/91	HIBERNIAN, Multicoloured (2000)	2.50 ☐
PTF115	*PTF115*	£5	4/91	HIBERNIAN, Multicoloured (1500)	5.50 ☐
PTF116	*PTF116*	£2	4/91	ST, JOHNSTONE, Multicoloured (2000)	2.50 ☐
PTF117	*PTF117*	£5	4/91	ST. JOHNSTONE, Blue and white (1500)	5.50 ☐

PTU - UNIVERSITY CARDS

No.	Ill.	Units	Date	Description	Value
PTU1	---	£2	4/91	EXETER UNIVERSITY, Multicoloured (20,000)	2.50 ☐
PTU2	---	£2	4/91	MANCHESTER UNIVERSITY, Multicoloured (10,000)	2.50 ☐
PTU3	---	£2	4/91	YORK UNIVERSITY, Multicoloured (9000)	2.50 ☐
PTU4	---	£4	4/91	YORK UNIVERSITY, Multicoloured (3000)	5.00 ☐

PTF55

PTF56

PTF57

PTF58

PTF59

PTF60

PTF63

PTF64

PTF65

PTF66

PTF67

PTF68

PTF69

PTF70

PTF71

PTF72

PTF100

PTF101

PTF102

PTF103

PTF104

PTF105

PTF106

PTF107

PTF108

PTF109

PTF110

PTF111

PTF112

PTF113

PTF114

PTF115

PTF116

PTF117

INTERNATIONAL PAYPHONES LIMITED

IPL began operation in the UK in January, 1990, with the installation of telephones in five hospitals and a shopping precinct. Cards were produced by Autelca, Switzerland. The unit is £0.10. The cards are given 'I' prefixes below. IPL has recently been taken over by IITL (Integrated Information Technology Ltd) and the IPL cards will no longer be issued. The telephones will operate in their coin mode only for the time being. It is not known whether IITL will itself issue cards eventually. The Scottish branch of IPL will continue to operate but as an independent company. Unused IPL cards are still available to collectors at the time of writing.

IC - COMPLIMENTARY CARD

No.	Ill.	Units	Date	Description	Value
IC1	*IC1*	(20)	7/89	Multicolour (480) Reverse as *IC1(reverse)*	50.00 ☐
IC2	*IC1*	(200)	7/89	Multicolour (20) (Differs only in coding)	--- ☐

ID - DEFINITIVE CARDS

No.	Ill.	Units	Date	Description	Value
ID1	*ID1*	20	11/89	Multicolour (?000)	2.50 ☐
ID2	*ID2*	20	11/89	Multicolour (?000)	2.50 ☐
ID3	*ID3*	20	11/89	Multicolour (?000)	2.50 ☐
ID4	*ID4*	20	11/89	Multicolour (?000)	2.50 ☐
ID5	*ID1*	50	11/89	Multicolour (?000)	6.00 ☐
ID6	*ID2*	50	11/89	Multicolour (?000)	6.00 ☐
ID7	*ID3*	50	11/89	Multicolour (?000)	6.00 ☐
ID8	*ID4*	50	11/89	Multicolour (?000)	6.00 ☐
ID9	*ID1*	100	11/89	Multicolour (?000)	11.50 ☐
ID10	*ID2*	100	11/89	Multicolour (?000)	11.50 ☐
ID11	*ID3*	100	11/89	Multicolour (?000)	11.50 ☐
ID12	*ID4*	100	11/89	Multicolour (?000)	11.50 ☐
ID13	*ID1*	150	11/89	Multicolour (2500?)	17.00 ☐
ID14	*ID2*	150	11/89	Multicolour (2500?)	17.00 ☐
ID15	*ID3*	150	11/89	Multicolour (2500?)	17.00 ☐
ID16	*ID4*	150	11/89	Multicolour (2500?)	17.00 ☐

Note. All values are found with all four face designs. The reverse is similar to *IC1(reverse)* above but with the number of units shown in the top right corner below the magnetic band. IC1 exists in both encoded and unencoded forms.

G - CLOSED USER GROUP CARDS

HM PRISON SERVICE CARDS. These cards are for use only in prisons and are not encoded for use in normal BT telephones. They are to prevent the use of ordinary BT cards as an inflated currency in prisons. Previously standard BT 20 unit cards (D13) were hand-stamped locally to differentiate them from smuggled cards as in G1 below. Various Home Office hand-stamps have apparently been used and cards bearing H.M.P.KIRKHAM/CANTEEN and NORTH SEA CAMP have also been found. There is more research to be done on this subject. Hand-stamps have also been found on S13, the 20 unit 1989 Winter card. Care should be taken, however, since forgeries are known to exist.

No.	Ill.	Units	Date	Description		Value
G1	*G1*	10	1988	Black / Green / silver (D12) (?000) Home Office	--- ☐	25.00 ☐
G1A	*(G1)*	20	1988	Black / Green / silver (D13) (?000) Home Office	--- ☐	15.00 ☐
G1B	*(G1)*	40	1988	Black / Green / silver (D13A)(?000) Home Office	--- ☐	35.00 ☐
G1C	*(G1)*	10	1988	Black / Green / silver (D12) (?000) HMP Kirkham	--- ☐	15.00 ☐
G1D	*(G1)*	20	1988	Black / Green / silver (D13) (?000) HMP Kirkham	--- ☐	15.00 ☐
G2	--	20	1988	Black / Multicolour (S13) (?000) Home Office	--- ☐	20.00 ☐
G2A	*(G1)*	10	1988	Black / Green / silver (D12) (?000) N. Sea Camp	--- ☐	25.00 ☐
G2B	*(G1)*	20	1988	Black / Green / silver (D13) (?000) N. Sea Camp	--- ☐	15.00 ☐
G2C	*(G1)*	10	1988	Black / Green / silver (D16) (?000) N. Sea Camp	--- ☐	15.00 ☐
G2D	--	20	1988	Black / Multicolour (S13) (?000) N. Sea Camp	--- ☐	20.00 ☐
G3	*G3*	20	6/89	Dark blue, green / silver, '2' 2.6mm (658,000)	--- ☐	1.00 ☐
G3(a)				Dark blue, green / silver, '2' 2.6mm, CN inverted	--- ☐	30.00 ☐
G3A	*(G3)*	20	1990	Dark blue, green / silver '2' 2.6mm,Thin letters	--- ☐	5.00 ☐
G4	*(G3)*	20	11/89	Dark blue, green / silver (76,000) '2' 3.1mm	--- ☐	1.00 ☐
G4A	*G4A*	20	1/91	SCOTTISH P.S. Blue, green / silver (250,000)	--- ☐	1.50 ☐

INMARSAT CARDS. These cards are for use on ships through the International Maritime Satellite communication system. Units are expensive which is why the cards carry only 12 of them. P&O is a shipping and ferry company while RFA stands for the Royal Fleet Auxiliary. These cards are understood to be still undergoing trials at the time of writing.

No.	Ill.	Units	Date	Description	Value	
G5	*G5*	12	???	P&O, Green / silver (5000)	35.00 ☐	10.00 ☐
G6	*G6*	12	???	RFA, Green / silver (5000)	35.00 ☐	10.00 ☐

Note. A standard £2 BT phonecard is reported to have been overprinted with the compliments of British Airways and their logo on the reverse for an executive function in, it is thought, 1986. No further details are known at present but it must be rare. Other private overprints are known.

OFFSHORE OIL AND GAS RIGS (PLATFORMS)

Currently nine companies operating in the North Sea have card-operated telephones installed for the private use of their employees. All have used optical cards made by Landis and Gyr (UK) and one, British Petroleum, has also used magnetic cards produced by GPT and Autelca. These were given the prefix 'R' in the first edition of this book and, because many collectors regard these cards as a self-contained group, it has been decided to retain this although strictly speaking they form a subset of Closed User Group cards. These cards are not generally available unused and are therefore no longer priced in that condition.

No.	Ill.	Units	Date	Description			
R1	*R1*	40	1984	BRITISH GAS: Green / silver (51,200)	--	☐	10.00 ☐
R1A	*(R1)*	40	7/89	Notched (20,000)	--	☐	5.00 ☐
R1A(a)				Control number inverted	--	☐	3.00 ☐
R2	*R2*	40	1984	BRITOIL, Green / silver (119,200)	--	☐	6.00 ☐
R2A	*(R2)*	40	1989	Notched (36,000)	--	☐	4.00 ☐
R2A(a)				Control number inverted	--	☐	3.00 ☐
R3	*R3*	60	1985	SHELL EXPRO: Red,etc., (1.5mm band) (48,000)	--	☐	80.00 ☐
R3A	*(R3)*	60	1987?	2mm white band (290,000)	--	☐	75.00 ☐
R3B	*(R3)*	60	1988?	4mm white band (200,000)	--	☐	40.00 ☐
R3B(a)				Control number inverted	--	☐	40.00 ☐
R3C	*(R3)*	60	6/88	3mm white band (50,000)	--	☐	20.00 ☐
R3D	*(R3)*	60	2/89	3mm white band, notched (190,000)	--	☐	10.00 ☐
R3E	*R3E*	120	9/89	Green, no band, notched (440,000)	--	☐	4.00 ☐
R4	*R4*	100	2/87	BRITISH PETROLEUM: Multicolour (40,000)			8.00 ☐
R4(a)	*(R4)*			With control number (51,025)			7.50 ☐
R4(b)	*(R4)*			With control number, Small notch.			7.50 ☐
R4B	*R4B*	40	2/90	Landis and Gyr card. Green / silver (48,000)	--	☐	4.00 ☐
R4C	*R4C*	20	4/91	IPL, Multicoloured			3.00 ☐
R4D	*R4C*	50	4/91	IPL, Multicoloured			4.00 ☐
R4E	*R4C*	100	4/91	IPL, Multicoloured			6.00 ☐
R4F	*R4C*	150	4/91	IPL, Multicoloured			8.00 ☐

Note. The values of the IPL BP cards are on the backs and they are all the same on the fronts.

No.	Ill.	Units	Date	Description			
R5	*R5*	60	1986?	NORTH SEA SUN OIL Co. Ltd: Green (30,000)	--	☐	3.00 ☐
R5A	*R5A*	60	1989?	SUN OIL BRITAIN Ltd: Green, Notched.	--	☐	2.00 ☐
R6	*R6*	100	8/88	MARATHON : Green / silver (15,000)	--	☐	60.00 ☐
R6A	*(R6)*	50	10/88	Notched (30,000)	--	☐	50.00 ☐
R6B	*(R6)*	100	10/88	Notched (15,000)	--	☐	5.00 ☐
R7	*R7*	(40)	1988	AMERADA HESS: Green, silver / silver (30.000)	--	☐	3.00 ☐
R8	*R8*	100	1990	TEXACO, Multicoloured (15,000)	--	☐	7.50 ☐
R9	--	40	1991	AMOCO, Green / silver (15,000)	--	☐	5.00 ☐

IC1

IC1(reverse)

ID1

ID2

ID3

ID4

G1

G3

G4A

G5

G6

R1

R2

R3

R4

R4B

R4C

R5

R5A

R6

R7

R3E

R8

P - PRIVATE/PROMOTIONAL CARDS

The cards below, issued by Plessey or GPT, UK, have been used at conferences and exhibitions in the UK and subsequently elsewhere.

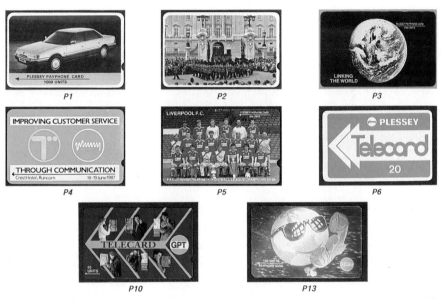

No.	Ill.	Units	Date	Description	Value
P1	*P1*	1000	6/87	ROVER, Multicoloured (1500)	50.00 ☐
P2	*P2*	1000	6/87	BUCKINGHAM PALACE, Multicoloured (1500)	50.00 ☐
P2(a)			16/3/87	Reverse-"Press luncheon, Ritz Hotel" etc.	200.00 ☐
P3	*P3*	1000	6/87	Multicoloured (1500)	125.00 ☐
P4	*P4*	(1000)	6/87	Blue, yellow, black, white (?000)	50.00 ☐
P5	*P5*	1000	1989	LIVERPOOL F.C., Multicoloured (?000)	40.00 ☐
P6	*P6*	20	198?	PLESSEY TRIAL CARD, Pale blue and white (?000)	50.00 ☐
P7	*(P6)*	40	198?	PLESSEY TRIAL CARD, Pale blue and white (?000)	50.00 ☐
P8	*(P6)*	100	198?	PLESSEY TRIAL CARD, Pale blue and white (?000)	50.00 ☐
P9	*(P10)*	10	1990?	GPT TRIAL CARD, Multicoloured (?000)	50.00 ☐
P10	*P10*	50	1990?	GPT TRIAL CARD, Multicoloured (?000)	50.00 ☐
P11	*(P10)*	100	1990?	GPT TRIAL CARD, Multicoloured (?000)	50.00 ☐
P12	*(P10)*	1000	1990?	GPT TRIAL CARD, Multicoloured (?000)	50.00 ☐
P13	*P13*	1000	1990	GPT HOLOGRAPHIC, "Multicoloured" (?000)	50.00 ☐
P14	--	1000	1990	'HAPPY BIRTHDAY', HOLOGRAPHIC, "Multicoloured" (?000)	50.00 ☐

Note: Many of the above cards are encoded with 1000 units of £0.10 i.e. they are £100 cards although they were never on sale. Most are also found without inscription these are samples or essays and usually not encoded. The promotional cards often do not have control numbers.

Telecom Eireann initially carried out field trials of three different systems in different cities – GPT cards were used in the Dublin area, cards by Autelca were used in Limerick and Landis and Gyr cards were used in Galway. Subsequently it was decided to adopt Schlumberger electronic payphones and Schlumberger and Gemplus smart cards were introduced in the summer of 1990. The trial cards are designated 'D' for Dublin, 'L' for Limerick and 'G' for Galway. The French smart cards have no special prefix except for a trial card by Gemplus which has been given the prefix F (for Forerunner) samples of which have occasionally appeared on the Paris market. There could be an analogous Schlumberger trial card but none has yet been reported. It has unfortunately been necessary to alter the numbering in a few places.

DD – DUBLIN DEFINITIVE CARDS

No.	Ill.	Units	Date	Description	Value
DD1	*(DD1)*	5	1987	Blue, deep blue, ochre / white (4570)	2.00 ☐
DD2	*(DD1)*	10	1987	.. .. (53,946)	2.50 ☐
DD2(a)			1990	Small notch (6000?)	2.50 ☐
DD3	*(DD1)*	20	1987	.. .. (49,135)	4.00 ☐
DD4	*(DD1)*	50	1987	.. .. (16,959)	10.00 ☐
DD5	*DD1*	100	1987	.. .. (4249)	20.00 ☐

SD – DUBLIN SPECIAL CARDS

No.	Ill.	Units	Date	Description	Value
SD1	*SD1*	10	1988	DUBLIN MILLENNIUM. Multicolour. (10,000)	6.00 ☐
SD2	*SD2*	100	24/10/88	FITCE, CORK. Blue, red, white. (960)	120.00 ☐

Note. The FITCE (Federation of International Telecommunication Engineers) cards were mostly handed out to the 600 delegates at their conference in Cork on 24 October, 1988. The others were later sold in Dublin.

DL – LIMERICK DEFINITIVE CARDS

No.	Ill.	Units	Date	Description	Value
DL1	*(DL1)*	5	02/89	Blue, green, black / white (5500)	2.00 ☐
DL2	*(DL1)*	10	02/89	.. .. (35,500)	2.50 ☐
DL3	*(DL1)*	20	02/89	.. .. (15,500)	5.00 ☐
DL4	*DL1*	50	02/89	.. .. (3250)	10.00 ☐
DL5	*(DL1)*	100	02/89	.. .. (1100)	25.00 ☐

SL – LIMERICK SPECIAL CARDS

No.	Ill.	Units	Date	Description	Value
SL1	*SL1*	20	21/4/89	IRISH MANAGEMENT INSTITUTE 89, As DL1 (250)	150.00 ☐
SL2	*(SL1)*	50	21/4/89	IRISH MANAGEMENT INSTITUTE 89, As DL1 (750)	400.00 ☐

DG – GALWAY DEFINITIVE CARDS

No.	Ill.	Units	Date	Description	Value	
DG1	*(DG1)*	5	25/7/89	Dark blue / white (5000)	2.00 ☐	2.00 ☐
DG2	*(DG1)*	10	25/7/89	.. .. (10,000)	2.50 ☐	2.50 ☐
DG3	*(DG1)*	20	25/7/89	.. .. (10,000)	3.50 ☐	3.50 ☐
DG4	*(DG1)*	50	25/7/89	.. .. (2000)	7.50 ☐	7.50 ☐
DG5	*DG1*	100	25/7/89	.. .. (1000)	15.00 ☐	15.00 ☐

ELECTRONIC (SMART) CARDS

C – COMPLIMENTARY CARDS

No.	Ill.	Units	Date	Description	Value
C1	*C1*	5	4/90	COMPLIMENTARY, TEDDY BEAR, Multicolour (GP) (10,000)	4.00 ☐
C1(a)	*(C1)*	5	2/91	Bear pinker, blue on reverse lighter (GP) (30,000)	1.00 ☐

D – DEFINITIVE CARDS

No.	Ill.	Units	Date	Description	Value
D1	*D1*	20	4/90	COTTAGE, Multicolour (Shades) (SI)(100,000)	2.50 ☐
D1(a)			1991	Gold contact (SI)(?????)	2.50 ☐
D2	*D2*	100	4/90	ROCK OF CASHEL, Multicolour, (GP) (10,000)	12.00 ☐
D3	--	10	4/91	RACING, Multicolour, (GP)(175,000)	2.00 ☐
D4	--	100	6/91	IRISH DANCERS, Multicoloured, (GP) (20,000)	12.00 ☐

S - SPECIAL CARDS

No.	Ill.	Units	Date	Description	Value
S1	*S1*	50	4/90	IRISH MANAGEMENT INSTITUTE 90, Multicoloured (SI)(2500)	15.00 ☐

Note. It was originally intended that there should be two IMI cards, 1500 of 20 units and 1000 of 50 units, as listed in the Stanley Gibbons Catalogue of Telephone Cards (1990). At the last moment it was decided to issue 2500 of only the 50 unit card.

No.	Ill.	Units	Date	Description	Value
S2	*S2*	50	4/90	IRISH PRESIDENCY OF EEC, Multicolour, (GP)(50,000)	6.00 ☐
S3	*S3*	5	17/3/91	St PATRICK'S DAY, Green, shades of blue (GP)(20,000)	1.50 ☐
S4	*S4*	50	3/91	DUBLIN-CULTURAL CAPITAL EUROPE, Multicol.,(GP)(50,000)	6.00 ☐
S5	—	20	4/91	COUNTY CORK - GAELIC FOOTBALL, Multicol., (GP)(25,000)	3.00 ☐
S6	—	20	4/91	COUNTY CORK - HURLING, Multicoloured, (GP)(25,000)	3.00 ☐
S7	—	5	6/91	TREATY OF LIMERICK 1691, Multicoloured, ( )(10,000)	1.50 ☐

F - FORERUNNER CARDS

No.	Ill.	Units	Date	Description	Value
F1	*F1*	1000	1987?	PLESSEY FOOTBALL CARD, Multicoloured (??)	50.00 ☐
F2	*F2*	??	1989?	GEMPLUS/CROUZET TRIAL CARD, Black, blue/white (GP)(??)	150.00 ☐

Note. The Plessey card shows the Irish national football team playing Brazil and was actually intended as an exhibition card for use in Brazil. It is, however, usually associated with Ireland and is therefore included here.

DD1

SD1

SD2

DL1

SL1

DG1

C1

D1

D2

S1

S2

S3

S4

F1

F2

ISLE OF MAN

OD1

D1

D2

D3

D4

D5

ISLE OF MAN

Manx Telecom is a separate company but is owned by British Telecom. Optical telephone cards were manufactured by Landis and Gyr in the UK and could also be used in British Telecom telephones throughout the UK. Only the two definitive cards listed below were issued. They have been given the prefix 'O' for optical. More recently the GPT magnetic system has been adopted. Some UK collectors are collecting the Isle of Man sets with matched control numbers.

OPTICAL CARDS (Landis and Gyr)

OD - DEFINITIVE CARDS

No.	Ill.	Units	Date	Description	Value	
OD1	*OD1*	10	4/87	Green / silver (14,000)	5.00 ☐	2.00 ☐
OD2	*(OD1)*	20	4/87	.. .. (13,600)	8.00 ☐	3.00 ☐

MAGNETIC CARDS (GPT)

D - DEFINITIVE CARDS

D1	*D1*	10	1/6/88	LAXEY WHEEL, Multicolour (12,082)	15.00 ☐	
D1(a)			1989	With control number (??????) '1IOMA...'	5.00 ☐	
D2	*D2*	20	1/5/89	PEEL CASTLE, Multicolour, Deep notch (5707)'3IOME...'	6.00 ☐	
D2(a)			12/89	Small notch, 4.5mm control (4809)'5IOMA...'	2.50 ☐	
D2(b)			2/91	Small notch, 4mm control (2409)'5IOMA...'	2.50 ☐	
D3	*D3*	100	7/9/89	GROUND STATION, Multicolour (2339)	15.00 ☐	
D4	*D4*	10	12/88	GREAT NORTH BEACH, Multicolour (12,000)	2.00 ☐	
D5	*D5*	20	12/89	CASTLE RUSHEN, Multicolour (10,742)	4.00 ☐	
D6	*D6*	30	12/89	PORT ST. MARY, Multicolour (12,000)	6.00 ☐	
D7	*D7*	100+10	4/91	Hologram issue (5193)	13.00 ☐	

S - SPECIAL/COMMEMORATIVE CARDS

S1	*S1*	10	1/6/88	TT RACERS 1st SERIES, Multicolour (#3) (6000)	25.00 ☐	
S2	*S2*	20	1/6/88	TT RACERS 1st SERIES, Multicolour (#2) (6000)	25.00 ☐	
S3	*S3*	20	1/6/88	TT RACERS 1st SERIES, Multicolour (#4) (6000)	25.00 ☐	
S4	*S4*	30	1/6/88	TT RACERS 1st SERIES, Multicolour (#1) (6000)	30.00 ☐	
S5	*S5*	15	1/12/88	CHRISTMAS '88, Multicolour (6000)	6.00 ☐	
S6	*S6*	10	1/6/89	TT RACERS 2nd SERIES, Multicolour (#6) (6000)	5.00 ☐	
S7	*S7*	20	1/6/89	TT RACERS 2nd SERIES, Multicolour (#7) (6000)	7.00 ☐	
S8	*S8*	20	1/6/89	TT RACERS 2nd SERIES, Multicolour (#8) (5923)	7.00 ☐	
S9	*S9*	30	1/6/89	TT RACERS 2nd SERIES, Multicolour (#5) (6068)	11.00 ☐	
S10	*S10*	10	2/10/89	2p Multicolour (8253)	2.00 ☐	
S11	*S11*	20	2/10/89	10p Multicolour (8419)	3.00 ☐	
S12	*S12*	20	2/10/89	13p Multicolour (8247)	3.00 ☐	
S13	*S13*	30	2/10/89	25p Multicolour (8376)	4.00 ☐	
S14	*S14*	10	14/2/90	15p Multicolour (15,000)	2.50 ☐	
S15	*S15*	10	14/2/90	18p Multicolour (15,000)	2.50 ☐	
S16	*S16*	20	14/2/90	32p Multicolour (15,000)	3.50 ☐	
S17	*S17*	30	14/2/90	34p Multicolour (15,000)	4.50 ☐	
S18	*S18*	40	14/2/90	37p Multicolour (15,000)	5.00 ☐	
S19	*S19*	10	5/90	TT RACERS 3rd SERIES, Multicolour (#10) (6000)	2.00 ☐	
S20	*S20*	20	5/90	TT RACERS 3rd SERIES, Multicolour (#11) (6000)	3.00 ☐	
S21	*S21*	20	5/90	TT RACERS 3rd SERIES, Multicolour (#12) (6000)	3.00 ☐	
S22	*S22*	30	5/90	TT RACERS 3rd SERIES, Brown, black, white (#9) (6000)	4.00 ☐	
S23	*S23*	20	8/5/91	ROUND TABLE NATIONAL CONFERENCE, Multicoloured (10,000)	2.50 ☐	
S24	*S24*	30	8/5/91	ROUND TABLE NATIONAL CONFERENCE, Multicoloured (10,000)	3.50 ☐	

D6

D7

S1

S2

S3

S4

S5

S6

S7

S8

S9

S10

S11

S12

S13

S14

S15

S16

S17

S18

S19

S20

S21

S22

S23

S24

S25

S26

S27

S28

S29

A1

A2

A3

A4

A5

A6

I1

I2

I3

I4

No.	Ill.	Units	Date	Description	Value
S25	*S25*	10	5/91	TT RACERS 4th SERIES, Multicolour (#) (6000)	2.00 ☐
S26	*S26*	20	5/91	TT RACERS 4th SERIES, Multicolour (#) (6000)	3.00 ☐
S27	*S27*	20	5/91	TT RACERS 4th SERIES, Multicolour (#) (6000)	3.00 ☐
S28	*S28*	20	5/91	TT RACERS 4th SERIES, Multicolour (#) (6000)	3.00 ☐
S29	*S29*	30	5/91	TT RACERS 4th SERIES, Multicolour (#) (6000)	4.00 ☐

A - ADVERTISING CARDS

A1	*A1*	10	9/12/89	DHL - EMMA, Multicolour (1500)	15.00 ☐
A2	*A2*	10	9/12/89	DHL - AMANDA, Multicolour (1500)	15.00 ☐
A3	*A3*	10	9/12/89	DHL - JACKIE, Multicolour (1500)	15.00 ☐
A4	*A4*	10	9/12/89	DHL - MARK, Multicolour (1500)	15.00 ☐
A5	*A5*	20	12/90	DHL, Multicolour (3000)	3.00 ☐
A6	*A6*	20	12/89	ELAN, Multicolour (3000)	3.00 ☐

Note. 750 of A5 and of A6 were issued by DHL in matched pairs in presentation packs. These have been offered by dealers at £100.

P - INTERNAL CARDS

The four cards below were presented to Manx Telecom employees in a presentation case and with a letter of authenticity to celebrate the completion of the modernisation of the Isle of Man telecommunications network. They have been classified as 'Internal cards' and given the prefix 'I' because, although sponsored by Manx Telecom, they were never formally available to the public. It is for collectors to decide whether these and the analogous Mercury 'party card', I1, should be included in their collections. The hologram in the corner of each card shows the logo of Manx telecom or a map of the island depending on the direction of the light.

I1	*I1*	10	31/10/90	FIBRE OPTICS, Red, shades of blue (500)	50.00 ☐
I2	*I2*	10	31/10/90	SATELLITE DISH, Multicolour (500)	50.00 ☐
I3	*I3*	10	31/10/90	OLD AND NEW PAYPHONES, Black, grey (500)	50.00 ☐
I4	*I4*	10	31/10/90	SWITCHING CIRCUITS, Green, black (500)	50.00 ☐

JERSEY

Jersey is the largest of the Channel Islands which lie off the French coast between France and England. Like the Isle of Man, the Channel Islands are not members of the European Community. Jersey has formal links with the UK but has its own Government and laws. Its telephone system is independent of British Telecom and the GPT magnetic telephone card system has been adopted. The cost of the first telephone card was reportedly reduced from £2 to £1.25 in June, 1989. The unit is of £0.05 so a 25 unit card costs £1.25, a 40 unit card £2 and so on. There seems to no real distinction between definitive cards and special cards in Jersey and all have therefore been grouped together under Definitives. All cards except D1 employ the GPT use-indication technology by which a small dent is made on a scale on the reverse at the end of each call. Used cards may thus easily be distinguished from unused cards and values are given for both used and unused.

D - DEFINITIVE CARDS

First Issue

No.	Ill.	Units	Date	Description		Value	
D1	D1	25	6/88	Dark and pale blue, yellow / white (10,000)		7.50 □	

Second Issue - Views

No.	Ill.	Units	Date	Description			
D2	D2	40	3/90	St. BRELADE'S BAY, Multicol.	(29,513)	3.00 □	1.50 □
D3	D3	40	4/90	ROCCO TOWER, Multicolour	(27,900)	3.00 □	1.50 □
D4	D4	80	4/90	PORTLET BAY, Multicolour	(25,000)	4.50 □	2.00 □

Third Issue - Castles

D5	D5	40	4/90	GOREY CASTLE, Multicolour	(25,000)	3.00 □	1.50 □
D6	D6	40	4/90	ELIZABETH CASTLE, Multicolour	(25,000)	3.00 □	1.50 □
D7	D7	80	4/90	GROSNEZ CASTLE, Multicolour	(25,000)	4.50 □	2.00 □

Fourth Issue - Steam Locomotives

D8	D8	25	4/90	DUKE OF NORMANDY, Multicolour (25,000)		2.50 □	1.50 □
D8(a)				Control larger (incl. above)		2.50 □	1.50 □
D9	D9	50	4/90	LA MOYE, Multicolour (25,000)		3.00 □	2.00 □
D9(a)				Control larger (incl. above)		3.00 □	2.00 □
D10	D10	50	4/90	SADDLETANK, Multicolour (25,616)		3.00 □	2.00 □
D10(a)				Control larger (incl. above)		3.00 □	2.00 □
D11	D11	100	4/90	St HELIER, Multicolour (27,321)		6.00 □	3.00 □
D11(a)				Control larger (incl. above)		6.00 □	3.00 □

Note. All the above issue show two different controls. The smaller can be 2.5mm (D9) or 3.0mm (D10) to 3.5mm while the larger may be 3.5mm (D10) or 4.0mm.

Fifth Issue - Jersey Wildlife Preservation Trust

D12	D12	25	12/90	SPECTACLED BEARS, Multicolour	(10,000)	1.50 □	1.00 □
D13	D13	50	12/90	LOWLAND GORILLAS, Multicolour	(11,047)	3.00 □	1.50 □
D14	D14	50	12/90	GOLDEN LION TAMARINS, Multicolour	(10,998)	3.00 □	1.50 □
D15	D15	100	12/90	CHEETAH, Multicolour	(10,887)	5.50 □	2.00 □

Sixth Issue - Jersey Parish Churches

D16	D16	40	3/91	ST BRELADE, Multicolour	(15,000)	2.50 □	1.50 □
D17	D17	40	3/91	ST CLEMANT, Multicolour	(15,000)	2.50 □	1.50 □
D18	D18	40	3/91	GROUVILLE, Multicolour	(15,000)	2.50 □	1.50 □
D19	D19	40	3/91	ST HELIER, Multicolour	(15,000)	2.50 □	1.50 □
D20	D20	40	3/91	ST JOHN, Multicolour	(15,000)	2.50 □	1.50 □
D21	D21	40	3/91	ST LAWRENCE, Multicolour	(15,000)	2.50 □	1.50 □
D22	D22	40	3/91	ST MARTIN, Multicolour	(15,000)	2.50 □	1.50 □
D23	D23	40	3/91	ST MARY, Multicolour	(15,000)	2.50 □	1.50 □
D24	D24	40	3/91	ST OUEN, Multicolour	(15,000)	2.50 □	1.50 □
D25	D25	40	3/91	ST PETER, Multicolour	(15,000)	2.50 □	1.50 □
D26	D26	40	3/91	ST SAVIOUR, Multicolour	(15,000)	2.50 □	1.50 □
D27	D27	40	3/91	TRINITY, Multicolour	(15,000)	2.50 □	1.50 □

D1

D2

D2(reverse)

D3

D4

D5

D6

D7

D8

D9

D10

D11

D12

D13

D14

D15

D16

D17

D18

D19

D20

D21

D22

D23

D24

D25

D26

D27

Everything for the Telephone Card Collector

ALBUMS
The Stanley Gibbons Telephone Card Album

Manufactured with the telephone card collector in mind, this fine but inexpensive album has a fully padded grey, 'leather-look' PVC binder appropriately blocked on the spine in gold.

The 8-pocket leaves are manufactured from 'Polyprotec' to ensure that your collection is preserved in perfect condition and the secure 4-ring mechanism will allow 300 plus cards to be safely stored in each album.

Supplied with ten leaves, extra packs of leaves also available.

Item 3523 GRY **Stanley Gibbons Telephone Card Album**   **£10.99**
Item 3524 **Extra leaves, per 5**   **£5.50**

The Mercurycard Luxury Telephone Card Album

For the Mercurycard collector Stanley Gibbons have produced a luxury album. It is a fully padded black 'grained' PVC Binder appropriately blocked on the front and spine in silver.

The 8-pocket, 'Polyprotec' leaves will keep your collection in perfect condition. The large capacity binder will allow 300 plus cards to be stored safely.

To enhance the presentation of your cards we have added black interleaving between each leaf.

Supplied with ten leaves and interleaving, extra leaves available.

Item 3548 **Mercurycard Luxury Telephone Card Album**   **£13.99**
Item 3550 **Extra leaves, per 5**   **£5.75**

Stanley Gibbons for Telephone Cards

We are pleased to say that we have been appointed agents or distributors for the following countries and telephone services:

MERCURY COMMUNICATIONS
incl. GPT–Paytelco.
MANX TELECOM
JERSEY TELECOMS
TELECOM AUSTRALIA
HONG KONG TELEPHONE
MACAO
CABLE & WIRELESS–Caribbean group
UNIPHONE SND (Malaysia)

Please telephone, write or fax for details of cards currently available.

**Stanley Gibbons Publication Ltd.
Parkside,
Christchurch Road,
Ringwood, Hants.
BH24 3SH
Great Britain**

Tel: 0425 472363,
Telefax 0425 470247

Postage and Packing:
£2.50 (UK) £5.00 (Overseas);